California

Everyday Mathematics®

CALIFORNIA

The University of Chicago School Mathematics Project

Student Math Journal
Volume 2

Grade **5**

Mc Graw Hill **Wright Group**

The McGraw·Hill Companies

The University of Chicago School Mathematics Project (UCSMP)

Max Bell, Director, UCSMP Elementary Materials Component; Director, *Everyday Mathematics* First Edition; James McBride, Director, *Everyday Mathematics* Second Edition; Andy Isaacs, Director, *Everyday Mathematics* Third Edition; Amy Dillard, Associate Director, *Everyday Mathematics* Third Edition

Authors
Max Bell, John Bretzlauf, Amy Dillard, Robert Hartfield, Andy Isaacs, James McBride, Kathleen Pitvorec, Peter Saecker, Noreen Winningham*, Robert Balfanz†, William Carroll†

*Third Edition only   †First Edition only

Technical Art	**Editorial Assistant**	**Teachers in Residence**
Diana Barrie	Rosina Busse	Fran Goldenberg, Sandra Vitantonio

Photo Credits
©W. Perry Conway/CORBIS, cover, *right*; Getty Images, cover, *bottom left*; ©PIER/Getty Images, cover, *center*.

Contributors
Tammy Belgrade, Diana Carry, Debra Dawson, Kevin Dorken, James Flanders, Laurel Hallman, Ann Hemwall, Elizabeth Homewood, Linda Klaric, Lee Kornhauser, Judy Korshak-Samuels, Deborah Arron Leslie, Joseph C. Liptak, Sharon McHugh, Janet M. Meyers, Susan Mieli, Donna Nowatzki, Mary O'Boyle, Julie Olson, William D. Pattison, Denise Porter, Loretta Rice, Diana Rivas, Michelle Schiminsky, Sheila Sconiers, Kevin J. Smith, Theresa Sparlin, Laura Sunseri, Kim Van Haitsma, John Wilson, Mary Wilson, Carl Zmola, Theresa Zmola

 This material is based upon work supported by the National Science Foundation under Grant No. ESI-9252984. Any opinions, findings, conclusions, or recommendations expressed in this material are those of the authors and do not necessarily reflect the views of the National Science Foundation.

California *Everyday Mathematics* Reviewers
Dr. Dale Oliver, Humboldt State University   Dr. Elizabeth Burroughs, Humboldt State University
Dr. Bill Jacobs, University of California, Santa Barbara   Dr. Alfred Manaster, University of California, San Diego

---

www.WrightGroup.com

Send all inquiries to:
Wright Group/McGraw-Hill
P.O. Box 812960
Chicago, IL 60681

ISBN 978-0-07-609827-9
MHID 0-07-609827-3

2 3 4 5 6 7 8 9 QWD 13 12 11 10 09 08

Contents

UNIT 7   Exponents and Negative Numbers

UNIT 8 Fractions and Ratios

UNIT 9   Coordinates, Area, Volume, and Capacity

UNIT 10 Using Data; Algebra Concepts and Skills

UNIT 11 Volume

UNIT 12   Probability, Ratios, and Rates

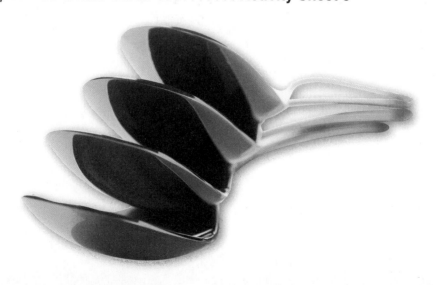

LESSON 7·1 Exponents

Math Message

1. Which is true: $4^3 = 12$, or $4^3 = 64$? Explain your answer.

   4×4×4=64   and   4×4×4≠12.

Exponential Notation

In exponential notation, the **exponent** tells how many times the **base** is used as a factor. For example, $4^3 = 4 * 4 * 4 = 64$. The base is 4, and the exponent is 3. The product, 64, is written in **standard notation.**

2. Complete the table.

Exponential Notation	Base	Exponent	Repeated Factors	Standard Notation
5^4	5	4	$5 * 5 * 5 * 5$	625
6^4	6	4	$6 * 6 * 6 * 6$	1,296
9^2	9	2	$9 * 9$	81
1^7	1	7	$1 * 1 * 1 * 1 * 1 * 1 * 1$	1
2^5	2	5	$2 × 2 × 2 × 2 × 2$	32

Exponents on a Calculator

3. Use your calculator to find the standard notation for the bases and exponents shown in the table. Record your keystrokes in the third column. Record the calculator display in the fourth column.

Base	Exponent	Keystrokes	Resulting Calculator Display
4	3		64
2	4		16
3	2		9
1	10		10

LESSON 7·1 Exponents continued

Each problem below has a mistake. Find the mistake and tell what it is.
Then solve the problem.

4. $5^2 = 5 * 2 = 10$

   Mistake: _____ $5^2 = 5 \times 5$ not 5×2. _____

   _____

   Correct solution: _____ $5^2 = 5 \times 5 = 25$ _____

5. $6^3 = 3 * 3 * 3 * 3 * 3 * 3 = 729$

   Mistake: _____ it is supposed to be 3^6. _____

   _____

   Correct solution: _____ $3^6 = 3 \times 3 \times 3 \times 3 \times 3 \times 3 = 729$ _____

6. $10^4 = 10 + 10 + 10 + 10 = 40$

   Mistake: _____ $10^4 = 10 \times 10 \times 10 \times 10$ _____

   _____

   Correct solution: _____ $10^4 = 10 \times 10 \times 10 \times 10 = 10,000$ _____

Use your calculator to write the following numbers in standard notation.

7. $7 * 7 * 7 * 7 = $ _____ 2401 _____

8. $15 * 15 * 15 * 15 = $ _____ 50,625 _____

9. $6^9 = $ _____ 10,077,696 _____

10. $5^8 = $ _____ 390,625 _____

11. $2^{12} = $ _____ 4,096 _____

12. 4 to the fifth power $= $ _____ 1024 _____

Write $<$, $>$, or $=$.

13. 10^2 ___ $<$ ___ 2^{10}

14. 3^4 ___ $=$ ___ 9^2

15. 1^2 ___ $=$ ___ 1^5

16. 5^4 ___ $>$ ___ 500

> **Reminder:**
>
> $>$ means *is greater than.*
>
> $<$ means *is less than.*

Number Sense 1.3; Mathematical Reasoning 2.4

LESSON 7·1   **Math Boxes**

---

1. Circle the fractions that are equivalent to $\frac{2}{3}$.

$\frac{10}{15}$ $\frac{4}{9}$ $\frac{9}{12}$ $\boxed{\frac{12}{18}}$ $\boxed{\frac{4}{6}}$

SRB 66 67

---

2. Peter has $\frac{3}{8}$ yard of ribbon. The costume he is making requires $\frac{3}{4}$ yard. How much more ribbon does he need?

_____ $\frac{3}{8}$ _____

SRB 68 69

---

3. Find the missing numerators or denominators.

a. $\frac{9}{15} = \frac{3}{5}$

b. $\frac{3}{24} = \frac{1}{8}$

c. $\frac{14}{21} = \frac{2}{3}$

d. $\frac{4}{8} = \frac{1}{2}$

e. $\frac{12}{18} = \frac{2}{3}$

f. $\frac{3}{21} = \frac{1}{7}$

SRB 59

---

4. Complete the "What's My Rule?" table, and state the rule.

Rule

⟋	☐
	100
9	0.9
50	5
	1.5
	0.5

SRB 231 232

---

5. Solve.

a. $(4 + 5) / 3 =$ _____

b. $(3 + 2) * (4 - 2) =$ _____

c. $((3 + 2) * (4 - 2)) / 2 =$ _____

d. $5 * ((5 + 5) * (5 + 5)) =$ _____

SRB 219

---

6. Leti kept the following record of time she spent exercising.

Day	M	T	W	Th	F
Hours	$\frac{1}{4}$	$\frac{1}{2}$	$1\frac{1}{4}$	0	$2\frac{1}{4}$

How many hours in all did she exercise?

_____ $4 \frac{1}{4}$ _____

SRB 70

LESSON 7·2 **Guides for Powers of 10**

Study the place-value chart below.

Periods									
Millions				Thousands			Ones		
Billions	Hundred-millions	Ten-millions	Millions	Hundred-thousands	Ten-thousands	Thousands	Hundreds	Tens	Ones
10^9	10^8	10^7	10^6	10^5	10^4	10^3	10^2	10^1	10^0

In our place-value system, the powers of 10 are grouped into sets of three: ones, thousands, millions, billions, and so on. These groupings, or periods, are helpful for working with large numbers. When we write large numbers in standard notation, we separate these groups of three with commas.

There are prefixes for the periods and for other important powers of 10. You know some of these prefixes from your work with the metric system. For example, the prefix *kilo-* in *kilometer* identifies a kilometer as 1,000 meters.

Use the place-value chart for large numbers and the prefixes chart to complete the following statements.

Prefixes	
tera-	trillion (10^{12})
giga-	billion (10^9)
mega-	million (10^6)
kilo-	thousand (10^3)
hecto-	hundred (10^2)
deca-	ten (10^1)
uni-	one (10^0)
deci-	tenth (10^{-1})
centi-	hundredth (10^{-2})
milli-	thousandth (10^{-3})
micro-	millionth (10^{-6})
nano-	billionth (10^{-9})

Example:

1 kilogram equals $10^{\boxed{3}}$, or one *thousand* , grams.

1. The distance from Chicago to New Orleans is about 10^3, or one _____, miles.

2. A millionaire has at least $10^{\boxed{}}$ dollars.

3. A computer with 1 gigabyte of RAM memory can hold approximately $10^{\boxed{}}$, or

   one _____, bytes of information.

4. A computer with a 1 terabyte hard drive can store approximately $10^{\boxed{}}$, or

   one _____, bytes of information.

5. According to some scientists, the hearts of most mammals will beat about 10^9, or

   one _____, times in a lifetime.

Number Sense 1.0, 1.1; Number Sense 1.3

LESSON 7·2   **Math Boxes**

1. Measure the length and width of each of the following objects to the nearest half inch.

   a. piece of paper

      length _____ in.   width _____ in.

   b. dictionary

      length _____ in.   width _____ in.

   c. palm of your hand

      length _____ in.   width _____ in.

   d. _____ (your choice)

      length _____ in.   width _____ in.

2. Amanda collects dobsonflies. Below are the lengths, in millimeters, for the flies in her collection.

   95, 107, 119, 103, 102, 91, 115, 120, 111, 114, 115, 107, 110, 98, 112   **SRB** 117–119

   a. Circle the stem-and-leaf plot below that represents this data.

Stems (100s and 10s)	Leaves (1s)
9	1 5 8
10	2 3 7 7
11	0 1 2 4 5 5 9
12	0

Stems (100s and 10s)	Leaves (1s)
9	1 5 8
10	2 3 7
11	0 1 2 4 5 9
12	0

Stems (100s and 10s)	Leaves (1s)
9	1 5 8 8 8
10	2 3 7 7 7
11	0 1 2 4 5 5 5
12	0

   b. Find the following landmarks for the data.

      Median: _____   Minimum: _____   Range: _____   Mode(s): _____

3. Measure ∠P to the nearest degree.

   ∠P measures about _____ .

   SRB 204

4. Calculate the sale price.

Regular Price	Discount	Sale Price
$12.00	25%	
$7.99	25%	
$80.00	40%	
$19.99	25%	

   SRB 51

LESSON 7·3 **Scientific Notation**

Complete the following pattern.

1. $10^2 = 10 * 10 = 100$

2. $10^3 = 10 * 10 * 10 = \underline{1000}$

3. $10^4 = \underline{10 \times 10 \times 10 \times 10 = 10000}$ $= \underline{\hspace{3cm}}$

4. $10^5 = \underline{10 \times 10 \times 10 \times 10 \times 10 = 100,000}$ $= \underline{\hspace{3cm}}$

5. $10^6 = \underline{10 \times 10 \times 10 \times 10 \times 10 \times 10 = 1,000000}$ $= \underline{\hspace{3cm}}$

Use the answers to Problems 1–5 to help you complete the following.

6. $2 * 10^2 = 2 * 100 = 200$

7. $3 * 10^3 = 3 * \underline{1,000} = \underline{3,000}$

8. $4 * 10^4 = \underline{4} * \underline{10,000} = \underline{40,000}$

9. $6 * 10^5 = \underline{6} * \underline{100,000} = \underline{600,000}$

10. $8 * 10^6 = \underline{8} * \underline{1000,000} = \underline{8,000,000}$

When you write a number as the product of a number and a power of 10, you are using **scientific notation.** Scientific notation is a useful way to write large or small numbers. Many calculators display numbers one billion or larger with scientific notation.

Example: In scientific notation, 4,000 is written as $4 * 10^3$.
It is read as four times ten to the third power.

Write each of the following in standard notation and number-and-word notation.

	Standard Notation	**Number-and-Word Notation**
11. $5 * 10^3 =$	$5,000$	
12. $7 * 10^2 =$	700	
13. $2 * 10^4 =$	20000	
14. $5 * 10^6 =$	$5000,000$	

Number Sense 1.1; Number Sense 1.3

LESSON 7·3 History of Earth

Geologists, anthropologists, paleontologists, and other scholars often estimate when important events occurred in the history of Earth. For example, when did dinosaurs become extinct? When did the Rocky Mountains develop? The estimates are very broad, partly because events like these lasted for many years and partly because dating methods cannot precisely pinpoint exact times from so long ago.

Scientists base their estimates on the geological record—rocks, fossils, and other clues—and on the bones and tools left long ago by humans. Below is a list of events prepared by one group of scientists. Different estimates are given by other scientists.

Use the place-value chart on the next page to help you write, in standard notation, how long ago the events below took place.

Example: Earth was formed about $5 * 10^9$ years ago. Find 10^9 on the place-value chart and write 5 beneath it, followed by zeros in the cells to the right. Then use the chart to help you read the number: $5 * 10^9 = 5$ billion.

Event	Estimated Time
1. Earth was formed.	$5 * 10^9$ years ago
2. The first signs of life (bacteria cells) appeared.	$4 * 10^9$
3. Fish appeared.	$4 * 10^8$
4. Forests, swamps, insects, and reptiles appeared.	$3 * 10^8$
5. The first dinosaurs appeared; the Appalachian Mountains formed.	$2.5 * 10^8$
6. Tyrannosaurus Rex lived; modern trees appeared.	$1 * 10^8$
7. Dinosaurs became extinct.	$6.5 * 10^7$
8. The first known human-like primates appeared.	$6 * 10^6$
9. Woolly mammoths and other large ice-age mammals appeared.	$8 * 10^5$
10. Humans first moved from Asia to North America.	$2 * 10^4$

Source: *The Handy Science Answer Book*

History of Earth continued

	Billion	100 M	10 M	Million	100 Th	10 Th	Thousand	100	10	One
	10^9	10^8	10^7	10^6	10^5	10^4	10^3	10^2	10^1	10^0
1										
2										
3										
4										
5										
6										
7										
8										
9										
10										

Work with a partner to answer the questions. Write your answers in standard notation.

11. According to the estimates by scientists, about how many years passed from the formation of Earth until the first signs of life?

_____

12. About how many years passed between the appearance of the first fish and the appearance of forests and swamps?

_____

13. According to the geological record, about how long did dinosaurs roam on Earth?

_____

LESSON 7·3

Expanded Notation

Each digit in a number has a value depending on its place in the numeral.

Example: 2,784

4 ones	or	4 ∗ 1	or 4
8 tens	or	8 ∗ 10	or 80
7 hundreds	or	7 ∗ 100	or 700
2 thousands	or	2 ∗ 1,000	or 2,000

C 4×10^0
8×10^1
7×10^2
2×10^3

Numbers written in expanded notation are written as addition expressions showing the value of the digits.

1. a. Write 2,784 in expanded notation as an addition expression.

2 thousands and 7 hundreds and 8 tens and 4 ones.

b. Write 2,784 in expanded notation as the sum of multiplication expressions.

$2 \times 1{,}000 + 7 \times 100 + 8 \times 10 + 4 \times 1$

c. Write 2,784 in expanded notation as the sum of multiplication expressions using powers of 10.

$2 \times 10^3 + 7 \times 10^2 + 8 \times 10^1 + 4 \times 10^0$

2. Write 987 in expanded notation as an addition expression.

9 hundreds and 8 tens and 7 ones.

3. Write 8,945 in expanded notation as the sum of multiplication expressions.

$8 \times 1{,}000 + 9 \times 100 + 4 \times 10 + 5 \times 1.$

4. Write 4,768 in expanded notation as the sum of multiplication expressions using powers of 10.

$4 \times 10^3 + 7 \times 10^2 + 6 \times 10^1 + 8 \times 10^0$

5. a. Write 6,125 in expanded notation as an addition expression.

6 thousands and 1 hundred and 2 tens and 5 ones.

b. Write 6,125 in expanded notation as the sum of multiplication expressions.

$6 \times 1{,}000 + 1 \times 100 + 2 \times 10 + 5 \times 1$

c. Write 6,125 in expanded notation as the sum of multiplication expressions using powers of 10.

$6 \times 10^3 + 1 \times 10^2 + 2 \times 10^1 + 5 \times 10^0$

LESSON 7·3   **Math Boxes**

---

1. Circle the fractions that are equivalent to $\frac{3}{8}$.

$\frac{6}{12}$ $\left(\frac{9}{24}\right)$ $\frac{8}{3}$ $\frac{4}{9}$ $\frac{15}{40}$

66 67

---

2. Charlene has $2\frac{5}{8}$ yards of fabric. The curtain she is making requires $3\frac{3}{4}$ yards. How much more fabric does she need?

$1\frac{1}{8}$

$\begin{array}{r} 3\frac{6}{8} \\ -\ 2\frac{5}{8} \\ \hline 1\frac{1}{8} \end{array}$

SRB 71

---

3. Find the missing numerator or denominator.

a. $\frac{4}{10} = \frac{2}{5}$ b. $\frac{42}{66} = \frac{7}{11}$

c. $\frac{35}{40} = \frac{7}{8}$ d. $\frac{9}{21} = \frac{3}{7}$

e. $\frac{5}{20} = \frac{1}{4}$ f. $\frac{6}{27} = \frac{2}{9}$

SRB 59

---

4. Complete the "What's My Rule?" table, and state the rule.

Rule

$\square \times 4 = \bigcirc$

◯	☐
28	7
16	4
1	$\frac{1}{4}$
20	5
0	0

SRB 231 232

---

5. Solve.

a. $\underline{\ \ 4\ \ } = 32 / (16 / 2)$ 8

b. $\underline{\ \ 1\ \ } = (32 / 16) / 2$ 2÷2=1

c. $(6.5 + 8.3) / (3 - 1) = \underline{\ 16.8\ }$ 14.8   2

d. $(4 * 12) + 8 = \underline{\ 56\ }$

SRB 219

---

6. Lilia did $2\frac{3}{4}$ hours of homework on Saturday and $\frac{3}{4}$ hour of homework on Sunday. What is the total time she spent on homework over the weekend?

$3\frac{1}{2}$

$3\frac{2}{4} = 3\frac{1}{2}$

SRB 70

---

1) NS 2.4   2) NS 2.3   3) NS 2.4
4) MR 1.1   5) NS 2.0   6) NS 2.3

LESSON 7·4

Parentheses and Number Stories

Math Message

1. Make a true sentence by filling in the missing number.

   a. $7 - (2 + 1) =$ ___4___

   b. $(7 - 2) + 1 =$ ___6___

   c. $2.0 * (7.5 + 1.5) =$ ___18.0___   [9 written above]

   d. $(2.0 * 7.5) + 1.5 =$ ___16.5___   [15 written above]

2. Insert parentheses to rewrite the following problem in as many different true sentences as possible.

   $6 * 4 - 2 / 2 = ?$

   $(6 × 4) - (2 ÷ 2) = 23$ [24 and 1 written above]

   $6 × (4 - 2) ÷ 2 = 6$

   $6 × 4 - (2 ÷ 2) = 23$

   $6 × (4 - 2 / 2) = 0$

Draw a line to match each number story with the expression that fits it.

3. **Story 1**

   Tom had 4 cans of soda.
   He went shopping and bought
   3 six-packs of soda cans.

   Story 2

   Tom had 4 six-packs of soda cans.
   He went shopping and bought 3 more
   six-packs of soda cans.

   Tom's Total Number of Soda Cans

   $(4 + 3) * 6$

   $4 + (3 * 6)$

LESSON 7·4   **Parentheses and Number Stories** continued

4. Story 1   **Number of Cookies Alice Ate**

Alice ate 3 cookies before going to a
party. At the party, Alice and 4 friends   3 + (45 / 5)
ate equal shares of 45 cookies.

Story 2

There was a full bag with 45 cookies
and an opened bag with 3 cookies.   (45 + 3) / 5
Alice and 4 friends ate equal shares
of all these cookies.

5. Story 1   **Number of Cookies Baked**

Mr. Chung baked 5 batches of cookies.
Each of the first 4 batches contained   15 * (4 + 5)
15 cookies. The final batch contained
only 5 cookies.

Story 2

In the morning, Mr. Chung baked
4 batches of 15 cookies each. In the   (4 * 15) + 5
afternoon, he baked 5 more batches
of 15 cookies each.

6. A grocery store received a shipment of 120 cases of apple juice. Each
case contained 4 six-packs of cans. After inspection, the store found that
9 cans were damaged.

Write an expression that represents the number of undamaged cans.

The grocery store received 2,871 cans.

120 cases
I case = 24 cans

$$\begin{array}{r} 120 \\ \underline{24} \\ 480 \\ 2400 \\ \underline{2,880} \end{array}$$

$$\begin{array}{r} 2,880 \\ \underline{-9} \\ 2,871 \end{array}$$

Math Boxes

---

1. Measure the length and width of each of the following objects to the nearest half inch.

   SRB 183

   a. journal cover

      length _____ in.   width _____ in.

   b. desktop

      length _____ in.   width _____ in.

   c. index card

      length _____ in.   width _____ in.

   d. _____ (your choice)

      length _____ in.   width _____ in.

---

2. a. Make a stem-and-leaf plot of the hand-span measures in Ms. Grip's fifth-grade class.

      163, 179, 170, 165, 182, 157, 154, 165, 170, 175, 162, 185, 158, 170, 165, 154

   b. Find the following landmarks for the data.

      Median: _____

      Minimum: _____

      Range: _____

      Mode(s): _____

   SRB 117–119

---

3. Measure ∠M to the nearest degree.

   ∠M measures about _____ .

   SRB 204

4. Calculate the sale price.

Regular Price	Discount	Sale Price
$8.99	20%	
$11.99	25%	
$89.00	20%	
$9.99	20%	

   SRB 51

LESSON 7·5 **Order of Operations**

Math Message

Robin asked her friends to help figure out how much money she needed to go to the movies. She asked her friends, "How much is 4 plus 5 times 8?" Frances and Zac said, "72." Anne and Rick said, "44."

1. How did Frances and Zac get 72? _They did $(4+5) \times 8 = 72$_

2. How did Anne and Rick get 44? _They did $4 + (5 \times 8) = 44$_

Robin's friends could not agree on who was right. Finally, Robin said, "I need to buy one under-12 ticket for $4, and 5 adult tickets for $8." Then Robin's friends knew who was right.

3. Who do you think was right? Explain your answer. _Anne and Rick were right, because $4 + (5 \times 8) = 44$ always do $(\times)$ first than $(+)$._

Use the rules for order of operations to complete these number sentences.

4. $100 + (500 / 2) =$ ___350___

   (250 over 500/2)

5. $24 / 6 + (3 * 2) =$ ___10___

   (4 over 24/6) (6 over 3*2)

6. $2 * 4^2 =$ ___32___

7. $(25 - 10) + (5 * 2) + (100 / 20) =$ ___30___

   (15 over 25-10) (10 over 5*2) (=15+5, 5 over 100/20)

8. $24 / 6 / 2 + 12 - 3 * 2 =$ ___?___

Insert parentheses in each of the following problems to get as many different answers as you can. The first one is done as an example.

9. $5 + 4 * 9 =$ ___$(5 + 4) * 9 = 81; 5 + (4 * 9) = 41$___

10. $4 * 3 + 10 =$ ___$(4 \times 3) + 10 = 22; 4 \times (3 + 10) = 52$___

11. $6 * 4 / 2 =$ _____

12. $10 - 6 - 4 =$ ___$(10 - 6) - 4 = 0; 10 - (6 - 4) = 8$___

Mathematical Reasoning 1.1

LESSON 7·5 **Story Problems**

1. Draw a line to match each story with the expression that fits that story.

Story 1

Marlene and her friend Kadeem each have eight pencils. They buy four more pencils.

Story 2

Marlene buys 2 eight-packs of pencils. Four free pencils come with each pack.

Number of Pencils in All

(2 * 8) + 4

2 * (8 + 4)

Write an open number sentence using parentheses to show the order of operations. Then solve.

2. LaWanda and two classmates decide to do research on horses. They find four books in the classroom and five books at the library that will help them. They divide the books equally so they can take the books home to read. How many books does each student take home?

Open number sentence: ___$(4 + 5) \div 3 =$___

Solution: ___3___

3. Coach Ewing has 32 snack bars. She divides them equally among the 16 members of the debate team. The team members share half of their snack bars with the opposing team. How many snack bars does each team member end up eating?

Open number sentence: ___$(32 \div 16) \div 2 =$___

Solution: ___1___

4. ___55___ $= 15 + 10 * 4$

5. $10 - 4 / (2 * 3) =$ ___$9\frac{2}{6}$___ $10 - \frac{4}{6}$

6. ___13___ $= 14 - 7 + 5 + 1$

7. ___28___ $= (18 - 11) * 3 + 7$
   29

8. $(9.5 * 2) / 0.5 + (45 / 5) =$ ___47___
   38

LESSON 7·5   Fractions in Simplest Form

A fraction is in **simplest form** if no other equivalent fraction can be found by dividing the numerator and the denominator by a whole number that is greater than 1. Another way to say this is that if the numerator and denominator do not have a common whole number factor greater than 1, then the fraction is in simplest form.

Every fraction is either in simplest form or is equivalent to a fraction in simplest form. A mixed number is in simplest form if its fractional part is in simplest form.

Example: $\dfrac{63}{108} = \dfrac{21}{36} = \dfrac{7}{12}$

The numerator 7 and the denominator 12 do not have a common whole number factor greater than 1, so $\dfrac{7}{12}$ is in simplest form.

1. a. Name the fraction for the shaded part of each circle.

 $\dfrac{1}{2}$

 $\dfrac{3}{6} = \dfrac{1}{2}$

 $\dfrac{4}{8} = \dfrac{1}{2}$

   b. Which fraction is in simplest form? ___A___

Name each fraction in simplest form.

2. $\dfrac{20}{30}$ ___$\dfrac{2}{3}$___

3. $\dfrac{7}{28}$ ___$\dfrac{1}{4}$___

$8\overline{)76}$ 9
-72
   4

4. $\dfrac{76}{8}$ ___$9\dfrac{1}{2}$___

Write each mixed number as a fraction.

5. $4\dfrac{2}{5}$ ___$\dfrac{22}{5}$___

6. $9\dfrac{3}{8}$ ___$\dfrac{75}{8}$___

7. $20\dfrac{2}{3}$ ___$\dfrac{62}{3}$___

Write each fraction as a mixed number.

8. $\dfrac{16}{7}$ ___$2\dfrac{2}{7}$___

9. $\dfrac{17}{3}$ ___$5\dfrac{2}{3}$___

10. $\dfrac{29}{4}$ ___$7\dfrac{1}{4}$___

Name each mixed number in simplest form.

11. $7\dfrac{10}{12}$ ___$7\dfrac{5}{6}$___

12. $3\dfrac{8}{32}$ ___$3\dfrac{1}{4}$___

13. $1\dfrac{9}{5}$ ___$2\dfrac{4}{5}$___

Number Sense 1.0

LESSON 7·5 Math Boxes

1. If you roll a six-sided die, what is the probability of getting...

   a. a three? $\frac{1}{6}$

   b. an odd number? $\frac{3}{6}$

   c. a multiple of 2? $\frac{3}{6}$

   d. a composite number? $\frac{2}{6}$

SRB 128 129

2. Tamara wants to buy the following items:
potato chips for $1.79
candy bar for $0.59
milk for $1.29
juice for $2.29

How much money does she need to pay for these items, without tax?

_$6.16_

$\begin{array}{r}2\;3\\1.79\\0.59\\1.29\\2.29\\\hline \$6.16\end{array}$

SRB 34–36

3. Use a calculator to rename each of the following in standard notation.

   a. $28^2 =$ _____

   b. $17^3 =$ _____

   c. $8^3 =$ _____

   d. $6^4 =$ _____

   e. $5^4 =$ _____

SRB 6

4. Read the graph and answer the questions.

Eladio's Scoring Record

   a. How many points did Eladio get in the first two games?

     _6_

   b. What is the range of Eladio's scores?

     _4_ $5-1=4$

SRB 124

5. Compare. Write < or >.

   a. 1.001 __<__ 1.011

   b. 8.090 __<__ 8.909

   c. 12.719 __<__ 16.791

   d. 27.334 __<__ 27.433

   e. 3.121 __>__ 2.211

SRB 32 33

6. Write each fraction as a mixed number or a whole number.

   a. $\frac{38}{3} =$ $12\frac{2}{3}$

   b. $11\frac{6}{7}$ $= \frac{83}{7}$

   c. $\frac{42}{6} =$ 7

   d. $2\frac{6}{11}$ $= \frac{28}{11}$

   e. $\frac{47}{12} =$ $3\frac{11}{12}$

SRB 23 62

LESSON 7·6 Making Line Graphs

Line graphs are often used to show how something has changed over a period of time.

The following steps can be used to make a line graph from collected and organized data.

Step 1: Choose and write a title.

Example:

Step 2: Decide what each axis is going to represent. Usually, the horizontal axis represents a unit of time (hours, days, months, years, and so on) and the vertical axis represents the data unit (temperature, growth, and so on).

Temperature at Noon (°F)

Days of the Week	Sun	Mon	Tue	Wed	Thu	Fri	Sat
Temperature (°F)	20	30	40	25	30	20	10

Step 3: Choose an appropriate scale for each axis.

Step 4: Draw and label each axis, including the scales.

Step 5: Plot each data point. **Step 6:** Connect the data points.

Temperature at Noon

1. Rossita's class keeps a record of books borrowed from the class library. A different student keeps the record each week. During Rossita's week, she collected and organized the data in this table. Use her data to make a line graph.

Books Borrowed from Class Library

Days of the Week	Mon	Tue	Wed	Thu	Fri
Number of Books Borrowed	10	5	4	8	12

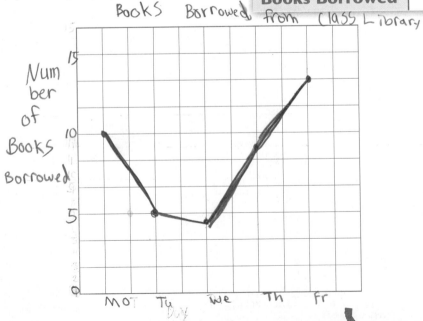

Statistics, Data Analysis, and Probability 1.0, 1.2

LESSON 7·6 Investigating Data in the American Tour

Line graphs can be used to make comparisons of two or more sets of data. Use the graph on page 365 of the *Student Reference Book* to answer the following questions.

1. What is the title of the graph?

   _____

2. What information is given on the horizontal axis?

   _____

3. What information is given on the vertical axis?

   _____

4. What two sets of data are being compared on the graph?

   _____

   _____

5. What was the life expectancy of a female born in 1940?

   _____

6. Use the information in the graph to write two true statements about life expectancy.

   _____

   _____

   _____

7. True or false? A man born in 1950 will live until the year 2015, when he will be 65 years old. Explain.

   _____

   _____

   _____

   _____

   _____

LESSON
7·6

Math Boxes

1. Measure the length and width of each of the following objects to the nearest half-inch.

   a. textbook

      length _____ in. width _____ in.

   b. seat of chair

      length _____ in. width _____ in.

   c. calculator

      length _____ in. width _____ in.

   d. _____ (your choice)

      length _____ in. width _____ in.

SRB
183

2. Make a stem-and-leaf plot of the following numbers:

120, 111, 137, 144, 121, 120, 95, 87, 120, 110, 135, 90, 86, 137, 144, 121, 120, 95, 87, 120, 110, 135, 90, 86, 143, 95, 141

Stems (10s)	Leaves (1s)

Find the landmarks.

Mode: _____

Median: _____

Range: _____

SRB
117–119

3. Draw and label a 170° angle.

SRB
204

4. Calculate the sale price.

Regular Price	Discount	Sale Price
$15.00	30%	
$4.50	20%	
$50.00	35%	
$12.95	60%	

SRB
51

 1) MG 1.4   2) SDAP 1.1   3) MG **2.1**
4) NS **1.2**

LESSON 7·7 **Positive and Negative Numbers on a Number Line**

Math Message

1. Plot each of the following bicycle race events on the number line below.
   Label each event with its letter. (*Hint:* Zero on the number line stands for the starting time of the race.)

   A Check in 5 minutes before the race starts.

   B Change gears 30 seconds after the race starts.

   C Get on the bicycle 30 seconds before the race starts.

   D The winner finishes at 6 minutes, 45 seconds.

   E Complete the first lap 3 minutes, 15 seconds after the race starts.

   F Check the tires 7 minutes before the race starts.

minutes

2. Mr. Pima's class planned a raffle. Five students were asked to sell raffle tickets. The goal for each student was $50 in ticket sales. The table below shows how well each of the five students did. Complete the table. Then plot the amounts from the last column on the number line below the table. Label each amount with that student's letter.

Student	Ticket Sales	Amount That Ticket Sales Were Above or Below Goal
A	$5.50 short of goal	~~-$5.50~~ $4.50
B	Met goal exactly	$50.00
C	Exceeded goal by $1.75	$51.75
D	Sold $41.75	$41.75
E	Sold $53.25	$53.25

$ sales above or below goal

LESSON 7·7 Comparing and Ordering Numbers

For any pair of numbers on the number line, the number to the left is less than the number to the right.

-10 is less than -5 because -10 is to the left of -5.
We use the < (less than) symbol to write -10 < -5.

+10 is greater than +5 because +10 is to the right of +5.
We use the > (greater than) symbol to write +10 > +5.

Reminder:

When writing the > or < symbol, be sure the arrow tip points to the smaller number.

Write > or <.

1. -5 __<__ 5

2. 10 __>__ -10

3. -10 __<__ 0

4. 14 __>__ 7

5. -14 __<__ -7

6. 0 __>__ $-6\frac{1}{2}$

Answer the following.

7. What is the value of π to two decimal places? __3.14__

8. -π = __-3.14__

List the numbers in order from least to greatest.

9. $-10, 14, -100, \frac{8}{2}, -17, 0$ __$-100, -17, -10, 0, \frac{8}{2}, 14$__

10. $-0.5, 0, -4, -\pi, -4.5$ __$-4.5, -4, -\pi, -0.5, 0$__

Answer the following.

11. Name four positive numbers less than π. __2, 0, 2.6, 0.4__

12. Name four negative numbers greater than -π. __-2, -0, -2.6, -0.4__

Number Sense **1.5**

LESSON 7·7   **Math Boxes**

---

1. Write the following number in standard notation.

One hundred fifty-four billion, two hundred twelve million, eighty-five thousand

154,212,085,000

SRB 5

2. Fill in the blanks.

246

a. $6 * (9 + 32) = (6 * \underline{40}) + (6 * \underline{1})$

168   504 = 672

b. $(8 * 21) + (8 * 63) = 8 * (\underline{21} + \underline{63})$

13

c. $3.5 * (17 - 4) = 35.5$

$(3.5 * \underline{1}) - (3.5 * \underline{0})$

d. $\underline{5} * (8 - 2) = (5 * 8) - (5 * 2)$

SRB 219

---

3. Shade $\frac{1}{4}$ of the fraction stick.

a. Is this more or less than $\frac{1}{2}$?

less $\frac{1}{2} > \frac{1}{4}$

b. Is this more or less than $\frac{1}{8}$?

More $\frac{1}{8} < \frac{1}{4}$

c. $\frac{1}{4} + \frac{1}{4} = \underline{\frac{2}{4}}$

SRB 66 67

4. Write the next two numbers in each number sequence.

a. 30, 60, 120, _240_, _480_

b. 112, 56, 28, _14_, _7_

c. $\frac{1}{7}, \frac{3}{7}, \frac{5}{7}, \underline{\frac{7}{7}}, \underline{\frac{9}{7}}$

d. $\frac{6}{4}, \frac{12}{4}, \frac{24}{4}, \underline{\frac{48}{4}}, \underline{\frac{96}{4}}$

SRB 230

---

5. A rental car company has 9 cars. If each car holds 17.6 gallons of gasoline, how much gasoline will the 9 cars hold all together?

___158.4___ gallons

$\begin{array}{r} {}^{6}{}^{5}17.6 \\ \times 9 \\ \hline 158.4 \end{array}$

SRB 38–40

6. Find the whole set.

a. 4 is $\frac{1}{8}$ of the set. _32_

b. 4 is $\frac{2}{5}$ of the set. _10_

c. 9 is $\frac{3}{7}$ of the set. _22.5_

d. 5 is $\frac{1}{3}$ of the set. _15_   24

e. 12 is $\frac{3}{8}$ of the set. $24 \frac{6}{8}$

SRB 75

LESSON 7·8 Using Counters to Show Account Balances

Use your $\boxed{+}$ and $\boxed{-}$ counters.

◆ Each $\boxed{+}$ counter represents $1 of cash on hand.

◆ Each $\boxed{-}$ counter represents a $1 debt, or $1 that is owed.

Your **account balance** is the amount of money that you have or that you owe.
If you have money in your account, your balance is **in the black.**
If you owe money, your account is **in the red.**

1. Suppose you have this set of counters.

   a. What is your account balance? ___$2___

   b. Are you in the red or in the black? ___black___

2. Use $\boxed{+}$ and $\boxed{-}$ counters to show an account with a balance of +$5. Draw a picture of the counters below.

   $$\begin{array}{r} 13 \\ -\ 8 \\ \hline 5 \end{array}$$

3. Use $\boxed{+}$ and $\boxed{-}$ counters to show an account with a balance of −$8. Draw a picture of the counters below.

   $$\begin{array}{r} +6 \\ -14 \end{array} \qquad \begin{array}{r} 6 \\ 14 \\ \hline -8 \end{array}$$

4. Use $\boxed{+}$ and $\boxed{-}$ counters to show an account with a balance of $0. Draw a picture of the counters below.

   $$\begin{array}{r} +2 \\ -2 \end{array} \qquad \begin{array}{r} 2 \\ -2 \\ \hline 0 \end{array}$$

Number Sense **2.1**, **2.2** ; Mathematical Reasoning 2.3

Date _____ Fri _____ Time _____

Use your counters to help you solve Problems 1–3. Draw ⊞ and ⊟ counters to show how you solved each one.

1. $+8 + (-2) =$ _+6_

2. $-4 + (-5) =$ _-9_

3. $-3 + (+7) =$ _+4_

Solve these addition problems.

4. $50 + (-30) =$ _+20_

5. _-20_ $= -50 + 30$

6. $-16 + 10 =$ _-6_

7. $-9 + (-20) =$ _-29_

8. _0_ $= -15 + 15$

9. $27 + (-18) =$ _9_

10. _-21_ $= -43 + (-62)$

11. $-17 + (-17) =$ _34_

12. -136

↓ in

Rule

out $= -12 +$ in

↓ out

[124]

13. The temperature at sunset was 13°C. During the night, the temperature dropped 22°C. Write a number model, and figure out the temperature at sunrise the next morning.

Number model: _____

Answer: _-9_

LESSON 7·8 Ruler Fractions

1. Mark each of these lengths on the ruler shown below. Write the letter above your mark. Point *A* has been done for you.

A: $2\frac{1}{16}$ in. *B*: $4\frac{3}{8}$ in. *C*: $3\frac{3}{4}$ in. *D*: $1\frac{7}{16}$ in. *E*: $2\frac{4}{8}$ in.

2. Measure the following line segments to the nearest $\frac{1}{16}$ of an inch.

a. ────────────────────────

_____ in.

b. ─────

_____ in.

c. ──────────────────────────

_____ in.

d. ─────────────────

_____ in.

3. Draw a line segment that is $4\frac{3}{16}$ inches long.

4. Draw a line segment that is $3\frac{1}{2}$ inches long.

5. Complete these ruler puzzles.

Example: $\frac{1}{4}$ in. = $\frac{x}{8}$ in. = $\frac{y}{16}$ in. $x =$ ___2___ $y =$ ___4___

a. $\frac{6}{8}$ in. = $\frac{x}{16}$ in. = $\frac{3}{y}$ in. $x =$ _____ $y =$ _____

b. $3\frac{2}{8}$ in. = $3\frac{m}{4}$ in. = $3\frac{4}{n}$ in. $m =$ _____ $n =$ _____

c. $\frac{6}{r}$ in. = $\frac{12}{s}$ in. = $\frac{t}{4}$ in. $r =$ _____ $s =$ _____ $t =$ _____

Number Sense 2.1; Algebra and Functions 1.0

LESSON 7·8 *500*

Materials   □   1 six-sided die

□   1 paper clip

□   pencil

Players   2

Object of the Game To be the first to reach 500

Directions

1. Use a paper clip and pencil for the spinner. Each player needs a score sheet.

2. Players take turns. One player is the "batter," and one player is the "catcher." Players alternate roles for each turn.

3. The batter spins. The catcher tosses the die.

4. If the catcher rolls an odd number, the action from the spin is a catch. If the catcher rolls an even number, the action from the spin is a drop.

   ◆ A catch is a positive number added to the catcher's score.

   ◆ A drop is a negative number added to the catcher's score.

5. Players keep track of the action from a spin, the points scored, and the total score for each round on their own score sheet.

6. The first player to reach 500 points wins.

Example:

Spin: Roll	Points Scored	Total Score
Grounder: catch	+25	25
Fly: drop	−100	−75
Two-bouncer: catch	+50	−25

LESSON 7·8   **Math Boxes**

---

1. If you roll a regular six-sided die, what is the probability of getting...

    a. a five? $\frac{1}{6}$

    b. a prime number? $\frac{4}{6}$

    c. an even number? $\frac{3}{6}$

    d. a multiple of 3? $\frac{1}{6}$

SRB 128 129

---

2. Solve.

Gino bought items at the store that totaled $13.95. He gave the cashier a $20 bill. How much change did he get back?

$6.05

SRB 34–36 243

---

3. Use a calculator to rename each of the following in standard notation.

    a. 3^{10} = _____

    b. 8^4 = _____

    c. 4^8 = _____

    d. 5^7 = _____

    e. 9^8 = _____

SRB 6

---

4. Read the graph and answer the questions.

Lunches Sold

    a. How many more lunches were sold on Wednesday than on Friday?

    5 lunches more.

    b. What is the range of the number of lunches sold?

    90 − 75 = 15

SRB 124

---

5. Compare. Write < or >.

    a. 4.344 $<$ 4.434

    b. 62.493 $>$ 60.943

    c. 0.126 $<$ 0.162

    d. 123.406 $>$ 123.064

    e. 342.010 $<$ 343.101

SRB 32 33

---

6. Write each mixed number as a fraction.

    a. $\frac{25}{7}$ = $3\frac{4}{7}$

    b. $\frac{17}{3}$ = $5\frac{2}{3}$

    c. $\frac{62}{9}$ = $6\frac{8}{9}$

    d. $\frac{16}{3}$ = $5\frac{1}{3}$

    e. $\frac{19}{2}$ = $9\frac{1}{2}$

SRB 62 63

---

1) MR 2.0   2) NS 2.1   3) NS 1.3
4) AF 1.1   5) NS 1.5   6) NS 2.5

LESSON 7·9   Finding Balances

Math Message

Use your ⊞ and ⊟ cash card counters to model the following problems. Draw a picture of the ⊞ and ⊟ counters to show how you found each balance.

Example:

You have 3 ⊟ counters. Add 6 ⊞ counters.

Balance = 3 ⊞ counters

1. You have 5 ⊞ counters. Add 5 ⊟ counters.

    Balance = _____0_____ counters

2. You have 5 ⊞ counters. Add 7 ⊟ counters.

    Balance = _____-2_____ counters

3. Show a balance of −7 using 15 of your ⊞ and ⊟ counters.

4. You have 7 ⊟ counters. Take away
    4 ⊟ counters.

    Balance = _____-3_____ counters

5. You have 7 ⊞ counters. Take away
    4 ⊟ counters.

    Balance = _____+3_____ counters

Date _____ Time _____

Adding and Subtracting Numbers

You and your partner combine your ⊞ and ⊟ counters. Use the counters to help you solve the problems.

1.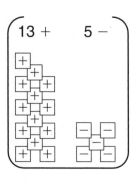

Balance = _____ +8 _____

If 4 ⊟ counters are subtracted from the container, what is the new balance?

New balance = _____ +4 _____

Number model: _____ +8 − ⁻4 = +4 _____

2.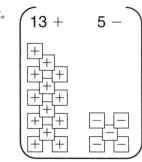

Balance = _____ +8 _____

If 4 ⊞ counters are added to the container, what is the new balance?

New balance = _____ +12 _____

Number model: _____ 8 + +4 = 12 _____

3.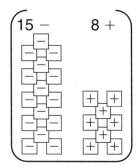

Balance = _____ ⁻7 _____

If 3 ⊞ counters are subtracted from the container, what is the new balance?

New balance = _____ +4 _____

Number model: _____ ⁻7 − +3 = 4 _____

4.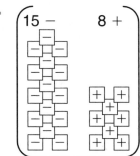

Balance = _____ ⁻7 _____

If 3 ⊟ counters are added to the container, what is the new balance?

New balance = _____ ⁻10 _____

Number model: _____ ⁻7 + ⁻3 = ⁻10 _____

Number Sense **2.1**, **2.2** ; Mathematical Reasoning 2.3

LESSON 7·9

Adding and Subtracting Numbers *continued*

5.

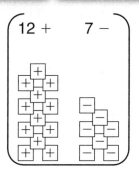

Balance = $+5$

If 6 ⊟ counters are subtracted from the container, what is the new balance?

New balance = -1

Number model: $+5 - {}^-6 = {}^-1$

6.

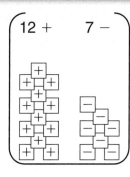

Balance = $+5$

If 6 ⊞ counters are added to the container, what is the new balance?

New balance = $+11$

Number model: $+5 + {}^+6 = {}^+11$

7.

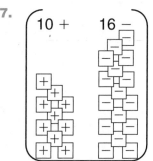

Balance = -6

If 2 ⊟ counters are subtracted from the container, what is the new balance?

New balance = _____

Number model: $-6 - {}^-2 = {}^-4$

8.

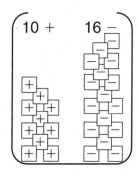

Balance = -6

If 2 ⊞ counters are added to the container, what is the new balance?

New balance = -4

Number model: $-6 + {}^+2 = {}^-4$

9. Write a rule for subtracting positive and negative numbers.

_____

_____

LESSON 7·9 Subtraction Problems

Rewrite each subtraction problem as an addition problem. Then solve it.

1. $100 - 45 =$ _____ $100 + (-45)$ $= {}^+55$

2. $-100 - 45 =$ _____ $-100 + 45$ $= {}^-55$ $\quad -100 + (-45) =$

3. $160 - (-80) =$ _____ $160 + (-80)$ $= {}^+80$ $\quad 160 + 80$

4. $9 - (-2) =$ _____ $9 + (-2)$ $= {}^+7$ $\quad 9 + 2$

5. $-15 - (-30) =$ _____ $-15 + (-30)$ $= {}^-45$ $\quad -15 + 30$

6. $8 - 10 =$ _____ $8 + 10$ $= 18$ $\quad 8 + (-10)$

7. $-20 - (-7) =$ _____ $-20 + (-7)$ $= {}^-27$ $\quad -20 + 7$

8. $0 - (-6.1) =$ _____ $0 - (-6.1)$ $= {}^-6.1$ $\quad 0 + 6.1$

9. The Healthy Delights Candy Company specializes in candy that is wholesome. Unfortunately, they have been losing money for several years. During the year 2006, they lost $12 million, ending the year with a total debt of $23 million.

a. What was Healthy Delights' total debt at the beginning of 2006? _____

b. Write a number model that fits this problem. $(\$\,{}^-12{,}000{,}000 \times 2) - \$1{,}000{,}000$

10. In 2007, Healthy Delights is expecting to lose $8 million.

a. What will Healthy Delights' total debt be at the end of 2007? _____ $\$15{,}000{,}000$

b. Write a number model that fits this problem. $(\$\,{}^-8{,}000{,}000 \times 2) - \$\,{}^-1{,}000{,}000 = 15$

Number Sense 2.1, 2.2

LESSON
7·9   **Math Boxes**

---

1. Make the following changes to the numeral 29,078.

Change the digit   28,074
in the ones place to 4,
in the ten-thousands place to 6,   69,078
in the hundreds place to 2,   69,274
in the tens place to 9,   69,294
in the thousands place to 7.   67,294
Write the new numeral.

_6_ _7_ , _2_ _9_ _4_

SRB
4

---

2. Solve.

$302 - m = 198$

$m =$ ___104___

Explain how you got your answer.

___I got my answer___
___by guess and checking___
___104 + 198 = 302___

SRB
219

---

3. Complete the table.

Standard Notation	Scientific Notation
300	$3 * 10^2$
3,000	$3 * 10^3$
4,000	4×10^3
500	5×10^2
7,000	$7 * 10^3$

SRB
8

---

4. Insert parentheses to make each sentence true.

a. $(48 \div 6) + (2 * 4) = 16$

b. $(48 \div 6) + (2 * 4) = 24$

c. $45 = (54 - 24 / 6 - 5)$

d. $0 = 54 - 24 / 6 - 5$

e. $30 = 54 - 24 / 6 - 5$

SRB
222 223

---

5. When Antoinette woke up on New Year's Day, it was −4°F outside. By the time the parade started, it was 18°F. How many degrees had the temperature risen by the time the parade began?

___24°F___

SRB
92 203

---

6. Write < or >.

a. $\dfrac{1}{4}$ _<_ $\dfrac{3}{8}$

b. $\dfrac{2}{7}$ _<_ $\dfrac{2}{5}$

c. $\dfrac{8}{9}$ _>_ $\dfrac{7}{8}$

d. $\dfrac{7}{12}$ _>_ $\dfrac{3}{6}$

e. $\dfrac{5}{12}$ _<_ $\dfrac{5}{11}$

SRB
66 67

LESSON 7·10 Addition and Subtraction on a Slide Rule

Math Message Find each sum or difference.

1. $13 - (+10) =$ _____

2. $13 - 10 =$ _____

3. $13 + (-10) =$ _____

Slide Rule Problems

Example 1: Addition

$$-3 + 6 = \_\_$$

Start — Face in the positive direction — Go forward 6

① Align the 0-mark on the slider with -3 on the holder.

Integer slider

2 1 0 1 2 3 4 5 6 7

−5 −4 −3 −2 −1 0 1 2 3 4

Integer holder

② Imagine facing in the positive direction on the slider. Go forward 6 (in the positive direction) on the slider. The 6 on the slider is aligned with 3 on the holder. This is the answer: $-3 + 6 = 3$.

Example 2: Subtraction

$$-6 - (-4) = \_\_$$

Start — Face in the negative direction — Go backward 4

① Align the 0-mark on the slider with -6 on the holder.

Integer slider

3 2 1 0 1 2 3 4 5 6

−9 −8 −7 −6 −5 −4 −3 −2 −1 0

Integer holder

② Imagine facing in the negative direction on the slider. Go backward 4 on the slider. (So you are actually going in the positive direction on the slider.) The 4 on the slider is aligned with -2 on the holder. This is the answer: $-6 - (-4) = -2$.

Use your slide rule to solve each problem.

4. $12 - 17 =$ _____

5. $12 + (-17) =$ _____

6. $10 - (-4) =$ _____

7. $10 + 4 =$ _____

8. $-10 - (-5) =$ _____

9. $6 - 13 =$ _____

10. $-2 + (-13) =$ _____

11. $-5 - 10 =$ _____

12. $-8 + 8 =$ _____

13. $-8 - 8 =$ _____

14. $-8 + (-8) =$ _____

15. $-8 - (-8) =$ _____

Number Sense 1.5, 2.1, 2.2

LESSON 7·10 Math Boxes

1. Write the following number in standard notation.

Nine billion, one hundred two million, three thousand sixty two

9,162,003,062 _____

_____

SRB 5

2. Fill in the blanks.

a. $(8 * 7) + (8 * 4) =$ __8__ $* (7 + 4)$

b. $23 * ($ __50__ $-$ __48.8__ $) =$ 23
   $(23 * 3.2) - (23 * 2)$ 3.2

c. __6__ $* (12 + 21) = (6 * 12) + (6 * 21)$
   72*12 6 = 198

d. $(9 -$ __1__ $) * (9 -$ __7__ $) =$
   __2__ $* (11 - 3)$

SRB 219

3. Shade $\frac{3}{8}$ of the fraction stick.

a. Is this more or less than $\frac{1}{2}$? __less__

b. Is this more or less than $\frac{1}{4}$? __more__

c. $\frac{3}{8} + \frac{1}{8} =$ $\frac{4}{8}$

SRB 66 67

4. Write the next two numbers in each pattern.

a. $\frac{1}{4}, \frac{3}{4}, \frac{5}{4}, \frac{7}{4}, \frac{9}{4}$

b. 6, 12, 24, __48__ , __96__

c. $-16, -13, -10,$ __-7__ , __-4__

d. $\frac{7}{5}, \frac{14}{5}, \frac{28}{5}, \frac{56}{5}, \frac{112}{5}$

SRB 230

5. A large jar of drink mix holds 1.75 kg. How much drink mix will 12 jars of the same size hold?

__21.12 kg__

```
   1.76
 ×  12
  3 5 2
 1 7 6 0
 21.12
```

SRB 38–40

6. 36 stamps per package. How many in . . .

a. $\frac{3}{4}$ of a package? __27__

b. $\frac{5}{6}$ of a package? __30__

c. $\frac{2}{9}$ of a package? __8__

d. $\frac{7}{12}$ of a package? __21__

e. $\frac{2}{3}$ of a package? __24__

SRB 75

Entering Negative Numbers on a Calculator

Math Message

1. Write the key sequence to display −4 on your calculator.

_____

2. What does the change-of-sign or change-sign key do?

_____

_____

Addition and Subtraction Using a Calculator

Use a calculator to solve each problem. Record the key sequence you used.

Example: **Calculator Entry**

$12 + (-17) =$ __−5__ $/2$ ⊕ ⊖ $/7$ (Enter)

3. $-10 - 17 =$ __7__   _____

4. $-10 + (-17) =$ _____   _____

5. $-27 + 220 =$ _____   I'll   do   with   dad

6. $19 - 43 =$ _____   _____

7. $-35 - (-35) =$ _____   _____

8. $72 + (-47) =$ _____   _____

9. $-35 - (-35) =$ _____   _____

10. $72 + (-47) =$ _____   _____

Number Sense 2.1, 2.2

LESSON 7·11   Entering Negative Numbers on a Calculator *cont.*

Solve. Use your calculator.

11. $3.65 - 2.02 =$ _____   **12.** $10 - (-5) =$ _____

13. $-901 - 199 =$ _____   **14.** $-7.1 + 18.6 =$ _____

15. $-2 + (-13) + 7 =$ _____   **16.** $2 - 7 - (-15) =$ _____

17. $41 / 328 =$ _____   **18.** $3 * 3.14 =$ _____

19. $-41 / 328 =$ _____   **20.** $-(3 * 3.14) =$ _____

21. $41 * (7 + 2) =$ _____   **22.** $41 * (7 + (-2)) =$ _____

Number Stories

23. A salesperson is often assigned a quota. A quota is the dollar value of the goods the salesperson is expected to sell. Suppose a salesperson is $3,500 below quota and then makes a sale of $4,700.

Did the salesperson exceed or fall short of his or her quota? _____

Write a number model to figure out by how much the salesperson exceeded or fell short. Use negative and positive numbers. Think about a number line with the quota at 0.

Number model: _____

Solution: _____

24. Stock prices change every day. Suppose on the first day a stock's price went up $\frac{1}{4}$ dollar per share. The next day it went down $\frac{1}{2}$ dollar. The third day it went up $\frac{5}{8}$ dollar.

Did the value increase or decrease from
the beginning of Day 1 to the end of Day 3? _____

Write a number model to figure out by how much the stock increased or decreased over the 3-day period. Use negative and positive numbers. Think about a number line with the Day 1 starting price at 0.

Number model: _____

Solution: _____

Number Sense **2.1**, **2.2**

LESSON 7·11 — Math Boxes

1. Make the following changes to the numeral 34,709.

90356
34

Change the digit

in the ones place to 6,
in the tens place to 5,
in the thousands place to 0,
in the ten-thousands place to 9,
in the hundreds place to 3.

Write the new numeral.

__90, 356__

2. Solve.

a. $m + 2,532 = 5,094$

$m = $ ___2562___

$$\begin{array}{r} 2532 \\ + 2562 \\ \hline 5094 \end{array}$$

b. $489.16 - n = 243.04$

$n = $ ___246.12___

$$\begin{array}{r} 489.16 \\ - 246.12 \\ \hline 243.04 \end{array}$$

SRB 219

3. Complete the table.

Standard Notation	Scientific Notation
60,000	6×10^4
500,000	$5 * 10^5$
400,000	$4 * 10^5$
700,000	7×10^5

SRB 8

4. Insert parentheses to make each sentence true.

a. $(22 + (3 / 3) - 2 = 21$

b. $(22 + 3 / 3 - 2) = 25$

c. $(18 / 6) + (3 * 5) = 18$

d. $(18 / 6) + (3 * 5) = 10$

e. $(5 + 7) * 3 / 9 = 4$

SRB 222 223

5. The temperature in Chicago at 5 P.M. was 35°F. By midnight, the temperature had dropped 48 degrees. What was the temperature at midnight?

___−13° F___

35
48

SRB 92 203

6. Write > or <.

a. $\dfrac{3}{8}$ ___<___ $\dfrac{3}{4}$

b. $\dfrac{9}{10}$ ___>___ $\dfrac{9}{16}$

c. $\dfrac{6}{7}$ ___>___ $\dfrac{5}{7}$

d. $\dfrac{10}{12}$ ___>___ $\dfrac{4}{6}$

e. $\dfrac{8}{9}$ ___>___ $\dfrac{6}{7}$

SRB 66 67

1) MR 1.2   2) AF 1.2   3) MR 2.6
4) MR 1.2   5) NS 2.1   6) NS 1.5

LESSON 7·12   **Math Boxes**

---

1. Circle the fractions that are equivalent to $\frac{2}{3}$.

$\frac{8}{9}$ $\boxed{\frac{20}{30}}$ $\boxed{\frac{14}{21}}$ $\frac{6}{10}$ $\boxed{\frac{12}{18}}$

SRB 59

2. Mike is making a cake. He needs $1\frac{1}{2}$ cups of sugar for the cake, and $\frac{1}{4}$ cup of sugar for the frosting. How much sugar does he need all together?

Open sentence: $\frac{1}{2} = \frac{2}{4}$ $1\frac{2}{4} + \frac{1}{4} =$

Solution: $1\frac{3}{4}$ of sugar

SRB 70

---

3. Show $\frac{2}{5}$ in at least two different ways.

 $\frac{4}{10}$, $\frac{8}{20}$, $\frac{16}{40}$, $\frac{32}{80}$

$\frac{}{50}$

SRB 59

4. Fill in the blanks.

$3\times$ $7 = 21$ $9 \cdot 12 =$

a. $3 * (3 + 4) = (\underline{3} * 3) + (\underline{3} * 4)$

11 135 - 36.99

b. $\underline{9} * (15 - 4) = (9 * 15) - (9 * 4)$

c. $(\underline{21} + 6) * (\underline{21} + 9) = 21 * (6 + 9)$

10

d. $\frac{1}{2} * (8 + 2) = (\underline{5} * 8) + (\underline{5} * 2)$

50

SRB 219

---

5. Use division to find equivalent fractions.

a. $\frac{2}{24} = \frac{1}{12}$

b. $\frac{6}{16} = \frac{3}{8}$

c. $\frac{2}{10} = \frac{1}{5}$

d. $\frac{10}{12} = \frac{5}{6}$

SRB 59

6. Insert $>$ or $<$.

a. $\frac{9}{14}$ _____$<$_____ $\frac{10}{3}$

b. $\frac{6}{21}$ _____$<$_____ $\frac{2}{6}$

c. $\frac{4}{11}$ _____$<$_____ $\frac{7}{16}$

d. $\frac{3}{7}$ _____$<$_____ $\frac{8}{18}$

e. $\frac{5}{24}$ _____$<$_____ $\frac{2}{10}$

SRB 66 67

LESSON 8·1 Comparing Fractions

Math Message

Write < or >. Be prepared to explain how you decided on each answer.

1. $\frac{3}{5}$ $\boxed{<}$ $\frac{4}{5}$ 2. $\frac{4}{5}$ $\boxed{>}$ $\frac{4}{7}$

| < means *is less than.* |
| > means *is more than.* |

3. $\frac{5}{9}$ $\boxed{<}$ $\frac{3}{7}$ 4. $\frac{7}{8}$ $\boxed{>}$ $\frac{6}{7}$

Equivalent Fractions

Cross out the fraction in each list that is not equivalent to the other fractions.

5. $\frac{2}{3}$, $\cancel{\frac{4}{6}}$, $\cancel{\frac{18}{24}}$, $\frac{20}{30}$

6. $\frac{1}{4}$, $\frac{2}{8}$, $\cancel{\frac{4}{20}}$, $\cancel{\frac{6}{24}}$, $\frac{8}{32}$

7. $\frac{3}{5}$, $\frac{6}{10}$, $\cancel{\frac{9}{20}}$, $\cancel{\frac{15}{25}}$

Write = or ≠ in each box.

8. $\frac{3}{5}$ $\boxed{\neq}$ $\frac{10}{15}$ 9. $\frac{6}{8}$ $\boxed{\neq}$ $\frac{16}{24}$

| ≠ means *is not equal to.* |

10. $\frac{15}{24}$ $\boxed{=}$ $\frac{5}{8}$ 11. $\frac{6}{14}$ $\boxed{\neq}$ $\frac{2}{7}$

Give three equivalent fractions for each fraction.

12. $\frac{6}{9}$ $\underline{\frac{12}{18}}$, $\underline{\frac{2}{3}}$, $\underline{\frac{4}{6}}$

13. $\frac{50}{100}$ $\underline{\frac{1}{2}}$, $\underline{\frac{500}{1000}}$, $\underline{\frac{5,000}{10,000}}$

14. $\frac{7}{10}$ $\underline{\frac{70}{100}}$, $\underline{\frac{7000}{1,000}}$, $\underline{\frac{700000}{100,000}}$

15. $\frac{15}{18}$ $\underline{\frac{150}{180}}$, $\underline{\frac{1500}{1800}}$, $\underline{\frac{15000}{18000}}$

Fill in the missing number.

16. $\frac{3}{4} = \frac{\boxed{27}}{36}$ 17. $\frac{3}{5} = \frac{\boxed{12}}{20}$ 18. $5 = \frac{\boxed{10}}{2}$

19. $\frac{\boxed{12}}{9} = \frac{24}{18}$ 20. $\frac{9}{12} = \frac{\boxed{27}}{4}$ 21. $\frac{16}{\boxed{20}} = \frac{8}{10}$

22. $\frac{2}{5} = \frac{6}{\boxed{15}}$ 23. $\frac{15}{\boxed{25}} = \frac{3}{5}$ 24. $\frac{4}{9} = \frac{16}{\boxed{36}}$

Write < or >.

25. $\frac{2}{5}$ $\boxed{<}$ $\frac{5}{10}$ 26. $\frac{3}{4}$ $\boxed{<}$ $\frac{5}{6}$ 27. $\frac{3}{8}$ $\boxed{>}$ $\frac{2}{7}$ 28. $\frac{3}{5}$ $\boxed{<}$ $\frac{4}{7}$

Number Sense 1.0, 1.5

LESSON 8·1 **Fraction Review**

1. a. Shade $\frac{1}{4}$ of the fraction stick.

   b. Use the fraction stick to find equivalent fractions: $\frac{1}{4} = \frac{2}{8} = \frac{4}{16}$

   c. $\frac{1}{4} + \frac{1}{4} = \frac{2}{4} = \frac{1}{2}$

2. a. Shade $\frac{3}{8}$ of the fraction stick.

   b. Is this more or less than $\frac{1}{2}$? ___less___

   c. Is this more or less than $\frac{1}{4}$? ___More___

   d. $\frac{3}{8} + \frac{1}{8} = \frac{4}{8} = \frac{1}{2}$

3. Joe had 2 granola bars. He ate $1\frac{1}{2}$ bars.

   a. Shade the part that he ate.

   b. Write the part he ate as a decimal. ___150.00___

4. Circle the decimal that is equivalent to each fraction. Use your calculator to help you.

   a. $\frac{1}{4}$ =   0.5   0.14   (0.25)   1.4

   b. $\frac{1}{10}$ =   1.10   (0.1)   (0.010)   0.50

   c. $\frac{2}{5}$ =   (0.4)   0.25   2.5   0.2

5. Lucy had 16 beads. Half the beads were red. One fourth were blue. The rest were white.

   a. Color $\frac{1}{2}$ of the beads red and $\frac{1}{4}$ blue.

   b. What fraction of the beads are white? ___$\frac{1}{4}$___

   c. Lucy put away all the white beads.

   What fraction of the remaining beads are red? ___$\frac{3}{4}$___

LESSON 8·1

Math Boxes

---

1. Make a circle graph of the survey results.

Favorite After-School Activity	
Activity	**Students**
Eat Snack	18%
Visit Friends	35%
Watch TV	22%
Read	10%
Play Outside	15%

Favorite After-School Activity
title

126 127

---

2. Write each numeral in number-and-word notation.

a. 43,000,000 ___43 million___

b. 607,000 ___607 thousands___

c. 3,000,000,000 ___3 billion___

d. 72,000 ___72 thousand___

SRB
4

---

3. Multiply.

a. $\frac{3}{8} * \frac{7}{9} =$ _____

b. $\frac{5}{7} * \frac{6}{11} =$ _____

c. $1\frac{3}{4} * 3\frac{2}{5} =$ _____

d. $2\frac{7}{6} * 1\frac{4}{5} =$ _____

e. $\frac{26}{4} * \frac{8}{6} =$ _____

76–78

---

4. Complete the "What's My Rule?" table and state the rule.

Rule

in x 5 = out

in	out
3	15
8	40
$\frac{1}{2}$	?
10	50
4	20

SRB
231 232

---

5. Find the area of the rectangle.

Area = $b * h$

14 cm

8 cm

Area: _____
(unit)

SRB
189

---

1) NS 1.2   2) MR 2.3   3) NS 2.4
4) MR 1.1   5) MG 1.4

LESSON 8·2 Adding Fractions

Math Message

Add. Write the sums in simplest form.

1. $\dfrac{3}{5} + \dfrac{1}{5} =$ _$\dfrac{4}{5}$_

2. $\dfrac{3}{8} + \dfrac{1}{8} =$ _$\dfrac{4}{8} = \dfrac{1}{2}$_

3. $\dfrac{2}{3} + \dfrac{2}{3} + \dfrac{2}{3} =$ _$\dfrac{6}{3} = 2$_

4. $\dfrac{3}{7} + \dfrac{5}{7} =$ _$\dfrac{8}{7} = 1\dfrac{1}{7}$_

5. $\dfrac{7}{10} + \dfrac{7}{10} =$ _$\dfrac{14}{10} = 1\dfrac{2}{5}$_

6. $\dfrac{5}{9} + \dfrac{7}{9} =$ _$\dfrac{12}{9} = 1\dfrac{3}{9} = 1\dfrac{1}{3}$_

7. $\dfrac{1}{6} + \dfrac{2}{3} =$ _$\dfrac{5}{6}$_

8. $\dfrac{2}{3} + \dfrac{2}{5} =$ _$\dfrac{16}{15} = 1\dfrac{1}{15}$_

9. $\dfrac{5}{6} + \dfrac{5}{8} =$ _$\dfrac{75}{48} = 1\dfrac{27}{48}$_

Adding Mixed Numbers

$\dfrac{10}{15} + \dfrac{6}{15} = \dfrac{16}{15}$ $\qquad$ $\dfrac{45}{48} + \dfrac{30}{48} = \dfrac{75}{48}$

Add. Write each sum as a whole number or mixed number.

10. $\quad 1\dfrac{3}{5}$
$\quad + 1\dfrac{1}{5}$
$\quad\; 2\dfrac{4}{5}$

11. $\quad 1\dfrac{1}{2}$
$\quad + \dfrac{1}{2}$
$\quad\; 2$

12. $\quad 2\dfrac{1}{4}$
$\quad + 3\dfrac{3}{4}$
$\quad\; 6$

Fill in the missing numbers.

13. $5\dfrac{12}{7} = 6\dfrac{5}{7}$

14. $7\dfrac{8}{5} = \boxed{8}\dfrac{3}{5}$

15. $2\dfrac{5}{4} = 3\dfrac{\boxed{1}}{4}$

16. $4\dfrac{5}{3} = 5\dfrac{\boxed{2}}{3}$

17. $12\dfrac{11}{6} = 13\dfrac{\boxed{5}}{6}$

18. $9\dfrac{13}{10} = 10\dfrac{\boxed{3}}{10}$

Add. Write each sum as a mixed number in simplest form.

19. $\quad 3\dfrac{2}{3}$
$\quad + 5\dfrac{2}{3}$
$\quad\; 9\dfrac{1}{3}$

20. $\quad 4\dfrac{6}{7}$
$\quad + 2\dfrac{4}{7}$
$\quad\; 11\dfrac{3}{7}$

21. $\quad 3\dfrac{4}{9}$
$\quad + 6\dfrac{8}{9}$
$\quad\; 10\dfrac{3}{9} = 10\dfrac{1}{3}$

LESSON 8·2 Adding Mixed Numbers *continued*

To add mixed numbers in which the fractions do not have the same denominator, you must first rename one or both fractions so that both fractions have a common denominator.

Example: $2\frac{3}{5} + 4\frac{2}{3} = ?$

◆ Find a common denominator. The QCD of $\frac{3}{5}$ and $\frac{2}{3}$ is $5 * 3 = 15$.

◆ Write the problem in vertical form, and rename the fractions.

$$
\begin{array}{r}
2\frac{3}{5} \\
+\ 4\frac{2}{3} \\
\hline
\end{array}
\quad \rightarrow \quad
\begin{array}{r}
2\frac{9}{15} \\
+\ 4\frac{10}{15} \\
\hline
6\frac{19}{15}
\end{array}
$$

◆ Add.

◆ Rename the sum. $6\frac{19}{15} = 6 + \frac{15}{15} + \frac{4}{15} = 6 + 1 + \frac{4}{15} = 7\frac{4}{15}$

Add. Write each sum as a mixed number in simplest form. Show your work.

1. $2\frac{1}{3} + 3\frac{1}{4} =$ _____

2. $5\frac{1}{2} + 2\frac{2}{5} =$ _____

3. $6\frac{1}{3} + 2\frac{4}{9} =$ _____

4. $1\frac{1}{2} + 4\frac{3}{4} =$ _____

5. $7\frac{1}{4} + 2\frac{5}{6} =$ _____

6. $3\frac{5}{6} + 3\frac{3}{4} =$ _____

Number Sense 2.0, 2.3

LESSON
8·2
Math Boxes

---

1. Add.

a. $\frac{1}{4} + \frac{2}{4} =$ _____

b. $\frac{3}{8} + \frac{1}{4} =$ _____

c. $\frac{1}{2} + \frac{1}{8} =$ _____

d. $\frac{2}{3} + \frac{1}{6} =$ _____

e. $\frac{2}{6} + \frac{2}{6} =$ _____

SRB
68

---

2. Use the patterns to fill in the missing numbers.

a. 1, 2, 4, _____, _____

b. 5, 14, 23, _____, _____

c. 4, 34, 64, _____, _____

d. 20, 34, 48, _____, _____

e. 100, 152, 204, _____, _____

SRB
230

---

3. The school band practiced $2\frac{3}{4}$ hours on Saturday and $3\frac{2}{3}$ hours on Sunday. Was the band's total practice time more or less than 6 hours?

_____

Explain. _____

_____

_____

SRB
71

---

4. Make each sentence true by inserting parentheses.

a. $18 - 11 + 3 = 10$

b. $18 - 11 + 3 = 4$

c. $14 - 7 + 5 + 1 = 13$

d. $14 - 7 + 5 + 1 = 1$

e. $14 - 7 + 5 + 1 = 3$

SRB
222

---

5. Solve.   Solution

a. $\frac{5}{9} = \frac{x}{18}$ _____

b. $\frac{8}{25} = \frac{40}{y}$ _____

c. $\frac{6}{14} = \frac{w}{49}$ _____

d. $\frac{28}{z} = \frac{7}{9}$ _____

e. $\frac{44}{77} = \frac{4}{v}$ _____

SRB
108 109

---

6. Circle the congruent line segments.

a. _____

b. _____

c. ___

d. _____

SRB
155

LESSON 8·3 Subtracting Mixed Numbers

Math Message

Subtract.

1. $3\frac{3}{4}$
    $-\ 1\frac{1}{4}$
    _____

2. $4\frac{4}{5}$
    $-\ 2$
    _____

3. $7\frac{5}{6}$
    $-\ 2\frac{2}{6}$
    _____

Renaming and Subtracting Mixed Numbers

Fill in the missing numbers.

4. $5\frac{1}{4} = 4\frac{\boxed{}}{4}$

5. $6 = 5\frac{\boxed{}}{3}$

6. $3\frac{5}{6} = \frac{\boxed{}}{6}$

7. $8\frac{7}{9} = \boxed{}\frac{16}{9}$

Subtract. Write your answers in simplest form. Show your work.

8. $8 - \frac{1}{3} =$ _____

9. $5 - 2\frac{3}{5} =$ _____

10. $7\frac{1}{4} - 3\frac{3}{4} =$ _____

11. $4\frac{5}{8} - 3\frac{7}{8} =$ _____

12. $6\frac{2}{9} - 4\frac{5}{9} =$ _____

13. $10\frac{3}{10} - 5\frac{7}{10} =$ _____

Number Sense 2.0, 2.3

Date _____   Time _____

Mixed-Number Spin

Materials ☐ *Math Masters*, p. 488

☐ large paper clip

Players   2

Directions

1. Each player writes his or her name in one of the boxes below.

2. Take turns spinning. When it is your turn, write the fraction or mixed number you spin in one of the blanks below your name.

3. The first player to complete 10 true sentences is the winner.

     Name   Name

_____ + _____ < 3   _____ + _____ < 3

_____ + _____ > 3   _____ + _____ > 3

_____ − _____ < 1   _____ − _____ < 1

_____ − _____ < $\frac{1}{2}$ _____ − _____ < $\frac{1}{2}$

_____ + _____ > 1   _____ + _____ > 1

_____ + _____ < 1   _____ + _____ < 1

_____ + _____ < 2   _____ + _____ < 2

_____ − _____ = 3   _____ − _____ = 3

_____ − _____ > 1   _____ − _____ > 1

_____ + _____ > $\frac{1}{2}$ _____ + _____ > $\frac{1}{2}$

_____ + _____ < 3   _____ + _____ < 3

_____ + _____ > 2   _____ + _____ > 2

LESSON 8·3   Math Boxes

---

1. Make a circle graph of the survey results.

Time Spent on Homework	
Time	**Percent of Students**
0–29 minutes	25%
30–59 minutes	48%
60–89 minutes	10%
90–119 minutes	12%
2 hours or more	5%

_____ title

126 127

---

2. Write each numeral in number-and-word notation.

a. 56,000,000 _____

b. 423,000 _____

c. 18,000,000,000 _____

d. 9,500,000 _____

SRB
4

3. Multiply.

a. $\dfrac{8}{11} * \dfrac{9}{10} =$ _____

b. $1\dfrac{5}{6} * 3\dfrac{7}{8} =$ _____

c. $2\dfrac{3}{4} * 2\dfrac{9}{5} =$ _____

d. $\dfrac{24}{5} * \dfrac{7}{3} =$ _____

e. $5\dfrac{1}{7} * 4\dfrac{1}{6} =$ _____

76 78

---

4. Complete the "What's My Rule?" table and state the rule.

Rule
_____

in	out
48	
40	5
1	$\dfrac{1}{8}$
	0
16	2

SRB
231 232

5. Find the area of the rectangle.

$$Area = b * h$$

12 m

6 m

Area: _____
(unit)

SRB
189

---

1) NS 1.2   2) MR 2.3   3) NS 2.4
4) MR 1.1   5) MG 1.4

LESSON 8·4 Exploring Fraction-Operation Keys

Some calculators let you enter, rename, and perform operations with fractions.

1. Draw the key on your calculator that you would use to do each of the functions.

Function of Key	Key
Give the answer to an entered operation or function.	
Enter the whole number part of a mixed number.	
Enter the numerator of a fraction.	
Enter the denominator of a fraction.	
Convert between fractions greater than 1 and mixed numbers.	
Simplify a fraction.	

Use your calculator to solve.

2. $5\frac{2}{9} + 6\frac{2}{5} =$ _____

3. $4\frac{16}{3} - 3\frac{1}{7} =$ _____

4. $26,342 \div \frac{2}{7} =$ _____

5. $\left(\frac{7}{8}\right)^2 * 14 =$ _____

6. In any row, column, or diagonal of this puzzle, there are groups of fractions with a sum of 1. Find as many as you can, and write the number sentences on another piece of paper. The first one has been done for you.

_____

_____

Example:

Number Sentence

$\frac{2}{6} + \frac{2}{8} + \frac{1}{6} + \frac{1}{4} = 1$

$\frac{2}{6}$	$\frac{1}{6}$	$\frac{3}{6}$	$\frac{1}{4}$	$\frac{2}{5}$	$\frac{5}{6}$
$\frac{2}{4}$	$\frac{2}{8}$	$\frac{2}{10}$	$\frac{2}{8}$	$\frac{2}{4}$	$\frac{1}{2}$
$\frac{3}{6}$	$\frac{1}{4}$	$\frac{1}{6}$	$\frac{1}{4}$	$\frac{2}{3}$	$\frac{3}{4}$
$\frac{1}{6}$	$\frac{4}{8}$	$\frac{1}{4}$	$\frac{1}{4}$	$\frac{1}{6}$	$\frac{1}{4}$
$\frac{1}{3}$	$\frac{2}{4}$	$\frac{2}{10}$	$\frac{2}{6}$	$\frac{2}{3}$	$\frac{1}{3}$
$\frac{5}{12}$	$\frac{1}{4}$	$\frac{1}{5}$	$\frac{3}{6}$	$\frac{1}{4}$	$\frac{3}{8}$

LESSON 8·4 **Math Boxes**

---

1. Add.

a. $\frac{1}{4} + \frac{1}{2} =$ _____

b. $\frac{1}{4} + \frac{5}{8} =$ _____

c. $\frac{4}{6} + \frac{1}{3} =$ _____

d. $\frac{1}{2} + \frac{1}{3} =$ _____

e. $\frac{1}{6} + \frac{1}{2} =$ _____

SRB
68

---

2. Use the patterns to fill in the missing numbers.

a. 2.1, 4.2, 8.4, _____ , _____

b. 50, 25, 12.5, _____ , _____

c. 3.4, 10.2, 30.6, _____ , _____

d. 1.5, 7.5, 37.5, _____ , _____

e. 1, 4, 9, _____ , _____

SRB
230

---

3. Max worked for $3\frac{3}{4}$ hours on Monday and $6\frac{1}{2}$ hours on Tuesday. Did he work more or less than 10 hours?

_____

Explain. _____

_____

_____

SRB
71

---

4. Make each sentence true by inserting parentheses.

a. $100 = 15 + 10 * 4$

b. $4 = 24 / 4 + 2$

c. $8 = 24 / 4 + 2$

d. $10 - 4 / 2 * 3 = 24$

e. $10 - 4 / 2 * 3 = 1$

SRB
222

---

5. Solve.   Solution

a. $\frac{m}{10} = \frac{45}{50}$ _____

b. $\frac{56}{64} = \frac{7}{n}$ _____

c. $\frac{k}{48} = \frac{3}{8}$ _____

d. $\frac{4}{30} = \frac{12}{p}$ _____

e. $\frac{2}{18} = \frac{a}{180}$ _____

SRB
108 109

---

6. Circle the congruent angles.

a.   b.

c.   d.

SRB
155

---

1) NS 2.3   2) MR 1.1   3) MR 1.1
4) MR 2.3   5) AF 1.2   6) MR 2.3

LESSON 8·5   Number-Line Models

Math Message

Use the number line above to help you answer Problems 1–10.

1. What is $\frac{1}{2}$ of 3? _____

2. What is $\frac{1}{4}$ of 2? _____

3. What is $\frac{3}{4}$ of 2? _____

4. What is $\frac{1}{3}$ of 3? _____

5. What is $\frac{1}{2}$ of $\frac{1}{2}$? _____

6. What is $\frac{1}{2}$ of $\frac{1}{4}$? _____

7. What is $\frac{1}{2}$ of $\frac{3}{4}$? _____

8. What is $\frac{1}{4}$ of $\frac{1}{2}$? _____

9. What is $\frac{1}{4}$ of $\frac{1}{4}$? _____

10. What is $\frac{1}{2}$ of $\frac{3}{8}$? _____

11. Explain how you figured out the answer to Problem 10. _____

_____

_____

_____

Solve.

12. $\frac{2}{3}$ of 12? _____

13. $\frac{2}{5}$ of 25? _____

14. $\frac{2}{3}$ of 90? _____

15. $\frac{3}{4}$ of 16? _____

16. $\frac{3}{4}$ of 28? _____

17. $\frac{3}{5}$ of 100? _____

18. $\frac{2}{3}$ of 18? _____

19. $\frac{3}{4}$ of 100? _____

20. $\frac{3}{5}$ of 50? _____

21. $\frac{5}{8}$ of 64? _____

LESSON 8·5 Paper-Folding Problems

Record your work for the four fraction problems you solved by paper folding. Sketch the folds and shading. Write an X on the parts that show the answer.

1. $\frac{1}{2}$ of $\frac{1}{2}$ is _____.

2. $\frac{2}{3}$ of $\frac{1}{2}$ is _____.

3. $\frac{1}{4}$ of $\frac{2}{3}$ is _____.

4. $\frac{3}{4}$ of $\frac{1}{2}$ is _____.

Number Sense 2.4, 2.5

LESSON 8·5 Paper-Folding Problems *continued*

Solve these problems by paper folding. Sketch the folds and shading. Write an X on the parts that show the answer.

5. $\frac{1}{3}$ of $\frac{3}{4}$ is _____.

6. $\frac{1}{8}$ of $\frac{1}{2}$ is _____.

7. $\frac{5}{8}$ of $\frac{1}{2}$ is _____.

8. $\frac{3}{4}$ of $\frac{3}{4}$ is _____.

LESSON
8·5 ## Fraction Spin

Materials   ☐ *Math Masters,* p. 471
                ☐ large paper clip

Players   2

Directions

1. Each player writes his or her name in one of the boxes below.

2. Take turns spinning. When it is your turn, write the fraction you spin in one of the blanks below your name.

3. The first player to complete 10 true sentences is the winner.

☐	☐
Name	Name

_____ + _____ < 1	_____ + _____ < 1
_____ + _____ > 1	_____ + _____ > 1
_____ − _____ < $\frac{1}{2}$	_____ − _____ < $\frac{1}{2}$
_____ − _____ > $\frac{1}{2}$	_____ − _____ > $\frac{1}{2}$
_____ + _____ < 1	_____ + _____ < 1
_____ + _____ < $\frac{1}{4}$	_____ + _____ < $\frac{1}{4}$
_____ + _____ > $\frac{1}{4}$	_____ + _____ > $\frac{1}{4}$
_____ + _____ = 1	_____ + _____ = 1
_____ − _____ < $\frac{1}{4}$	_____ − _____ < $\frac{1}{4}$
_____ − _____ > $\frac{1}{4}$	_____ − _____ > $\frac{1}{4}$
_____ + _____ < $\frac{3}{4}$	_____ + _____ < $\frac{3}{4}$
_____ + _____ > $\frac{3}{4}$	_____ + _____ > $\frac{3}{4}$

Number Sense 2.0

Date _____ Time _____

1. Complete.

a. $\dfrac{2}{3} = \dfrac{\boxed{}}{24} = \dfrac{\boxed{}}{36}$

b. $\dfrac{1}{8} = \dfrac{\boxed{}}{24} = \dfrac{\boxed{}}{32}$

c. $\dfrac{2}{5} = \dfrac{\boxed{}}{25} = \dfrac{12}{\boxed{}}$

d. $\dfrac{1}{6} = \dfrac{3}{\boxed{}} = \dfrac{4}{\boxed{}}$

SRB 108 109

2. Write *true* or *false* for each number sentence.

a. $16 - (3 + 5) = 18$ _____

b. $(4 + 2) * 5 = 30$ _____

c. $100 \div (25 + 25) + 5 = 7$ _____

d. $15 - 4 * 3 + 2 = 35$ _____

e. $(40 - 2^2) \div 6 = 6$ _____

SRB 222 223

3. Use the grid on the right to locate the following objects on the map. The first one has been done for you.

a. Fifth grader _D4_

b. Boat _____

c. Car _____

d. House _____

e. Tree _____

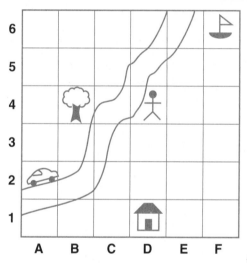

SRB 208

4. Circle any triangles that look like equilateral triangles.

Write a definition of an equilateral triangle.

_____

_____

_____

SRB 144

5. The soup can and cereal box below represent geometric solids. Name each of these solids.

a.

b.

_____   _____

SRB 147–149

**LESSON
8·6**   # Fraction Multiplication

Math Message

1. Use the rectangle at the right to
   sketch how you would fold paper
   to help you find $\frac{1}{3}$ of $\frac{2}{3}$.

   What is $\frac{1}{3}$ of $\frac{2}{3}$? _____

2. Use the rectangle at the right to
   sketch how you would fold paper
   to help you find $\frac{1}{4}$ of $\frac{3}{5}$.

   What is $\frac{1}{4}$ of $\frac{3}{5}$? _____

3. Rewrite $\frac{2}{3}$ of $\frac{3}{4}$ using the multiplication symbol *. _____

4. Rewrite the following fraction-of-fraction problems using the multiplication symbol *.

   a. $\frac{1}{4}$ of $\frac{1}{3}$ _____   b. $\frac{4}{5}$ of $\frac{2}{3}$ _____

   c. $\frac{1}{6}$ of $\frac{1}{4}$ _____   d. $\frac{3}{7}$ of $\frac{2}{5}$ _____

Number Sense 2.4; Number Sense 2.5

Date _____   Time _____

1. Use the rectangle at the right to find $\frac{2}{3} * \frac{3}{4}$.

$\frac{2}{3} * \frac{3}{4} =$ _____

Your completed drawing in Problem 1 is called an **area model.**
Use area models to complete the remaining problems.

2.

$\frac{2}{3} * \frac{1}{5} =$ _____

3.

$\frac{3}{4} * \frac{2}{5} =$ _____

4.

$\frac{1}{4} * \frac{5}{6} =$ _____

5.

$\frac{3}{8} * \frac{3}{5} =$ _____

6.

$\frac{1}{2} * \frac{5}{8} =$ _____

7.

$\frac{5}{6} * \frac{4}{5} =$ _____

Explain how you sketched and shaded the rectangle to solve Problem 7.

_____

_____

_____

_____

_____

LESSON 8·6   An Algorithm for Fraction Multiplication

1. Look carefully at the fractions on journal page 265. What is the relationship between the numerators and the denominators of the two fractions being multiplied and the numerator and the denominator of their product?

_____

_____

_____

_____

2. Describe a way to multiply two fractions. _____

_____

_____

_____

3. Multiply the following fractions using the algorithm discussed in class.

   a. $\frac{1}{3} * \frac{1}{5} =$ _____

   b. $\frac{2}{3} * \frac{1}{3} =$ _____

   c. $\frac{3}{10} * \frac{7}{10} =$ _____

   d. $\frac{5}{8} * \frac{1}{4} =$ _____

   e. $\frac{3}{8} * \frac{5}{6} =$ _____

   f. $\frac{2}{5} * \frac{5}{12} =$ _____

   g. $\frac{4}{5} * \frac{2}{5} =$ _____

   h. $\frac{4}{9} * \frac{3}{7} =$ _____

   i. $\frac{2}{4} * \frac{4}{8} =$ _____

   j. $\frac{3}{7} * \frac{5}{9} =$ _____

   k. $\frac{7}{9} * \frac{2}{6} =$ _____

   l. $\frac{2}{7} * \frac{9}{10} =$ _____

4. Girls are one-half of the fifth-grade class. Two-tenths of these girls have red hair. Red-haired girls are what fraction of the fifth-grade class?

_____

Number Sense 2.4; Number Sense 2.5

LESSON 8·6   **Math Boxes**

---

1. The digit in the hundreds place is a square number, and it is odd.
   The digit in the tens place is 1 more than the square root of 16.
   The digit in the hundredths place is 0.1 larger than $\frac{1}{10}$ of the digit in the hundreds place.
   The digit in the thousandths place is equivalent to $\frac{30}{5}$.
   The other digits are all 2s.

   ___ ___ ___ . ___ ___ ___

   Write this number in expanded notation. _____

   SRB 4

---

2. Write 3 equivalent fractions for each number.

   a. $\frac{2}{5}$ = _____

   b. $\frac{4}{7}$ = _____

   c. $\frac{1}{2}$ = _____

   d. $\frac{40}{50}$ = _____

   e. $\frac{25}{75}$ = _____

   SRB 59

3. Jon spent $24\frac{1}{4}$ hours reading in March and $15\frac{1}{2}$ hours reading in April. How many more hours did he spend reading in March?

   Number model: _____

   Answer: _____

   SRB 71 72

---

4. Complete.

   a. $\frac{10}{100} = \frac{\boxed{}}{10}$

   b. $\frac{8}{100} = \frac{\boxed{}}{25}$

   c. $\frac{5}{20} = \frac{1}{\boxed{}}$

   d. $\frac{10}{12} = \frac{5}{\boxed{}}$

   SRB 108 109

5. Use your Geometry Template to draw a trapezoid.

   How does the trapezoid you've drawn differ from other quadrangles on the Geometry Template?

   _____

   _____

   SRB 134–136

LESSON 8·7   **A Blast from the Past**

1. From *Kindergarten Everyday Mathematics:*

   This slice of pizza is what
   fraction of the whole pizza? _____

2. From *First Grade Everyday Mathematics:*

   Write a fraction in each part of the diagrams below. Then color the figures as directed.

   a.

   Color $\frac{3}{4}$.

   b.

   Color $\frac{2}{3}$.

   c.

   Color $\frac{2}{2}$.

3. From *Second Grade Everyday Mathematics:*

   a.

   Color $\frac{1}{4}$ of the beads.

   b.

   Color $\frac{1}{8}$ of the beads.

4. From *Third Grade Everyday Mathematics:*

   a. $\frac{1}{2}$ of $\frac{1}{4}$ = _____

   b. $\frac{1}{8}$ of $\frac{1}{2}$ = _____

   c. $\frac{1}{2}$ of $\frac{1}{8}$ = _____

5. From *Fourth Grade Everyday Mathematics:*

   Cross out $\frac{5}{6}$ of the dimes.

Number Sense 1.0, 2.0, 2.4, 2.5; Mathematical Reasoning 2.3

LESSON 8·7 Area Models

Draw an area model for each product. Then write the product as a fraction or as a mixed number.

Example: $\frac{2}{3} * 2 = $ ___$\frac{4}{3}$, or $1\frac{1}{3}$___

1. $\frac{1}{3} * 4 = $ _____

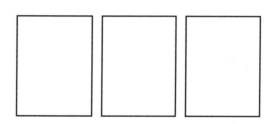

2. $\frac{1}{4} * 3 = $ _____

3. $2 * \frac{3}{5} = $ _____

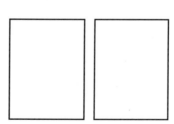

4. $\frac{3}{8} * 3 = $ _____

LESSON 8·7 Using the Fraction Multiplication Algorithm

An Algorithm for Fraction Multiplication

$$\frac{a}{b} * \frac{c}{d} = \frac{a * c}{b * d}$$

The denominator of the product is the product of the denominators, and the numerator of the product is the product of the numerators.

Example: $\frac{2}{3} * 2$

$$\frac{2}{3} * 2 = \frac{2}{3} * \frac{2}{1} \qquad \text{Think of 2 as } \frac{2}{1}.$$

$$= \frac{2 * 2}{3 * 1} \qquad \text{Apply the algorithm.}$$

$$= \frac{4}{3}, \text{ or } 1\frac{1}{3} \qquad \text{Calculate the numerator and denominator.}$$

Use the fraction multiplication algorithm to calculate the following products.

1. $\frac{3}{4} * 6 =$ $\dfrac{3 \cdot 6}{4 \cdot 1} = \dfrac{3 \cdot 6^{3}}{4_{2}} = \dfrac{9}{2} = 4\frac{1}{2}$

2. $\frac{7}{8} * 3 =$ _____

3. $\frac{3}{10} * 5 =$ $\dfrac{3 \cdot 5^{1}}{10_{2}} = \dfrac{3}{2}$

4. $6 * \frac{4}{5} =$ $\dfrac{6.4}{5}$

---

5. Use the given rule to complete the table.

6. What is the rule for the table below?

Rule
$\triangle = \square * \frac{3}{5}$

in (□)	out (△)
$\frac{1}{2}$	
2	
$\frac{4}{5}$	
$\frac{3}{4}$	
3	

Rule

in (□)	out (△)
$\frac{2}{3}$	$\frac{2}{6}$
$\frac{3}{4}$	$\frac{3}{8}$
$\frac{7}{8}$	$\frac{7}{16}$
3	$1\frac{1}{2}$

Number Sense 2.4; Number Sense 2.5; Algebra and Functions 1.0

LESSON 8·7   **Math Boxes**

---

1. Complete.

a. $\dfrac{1}{5} = \dfrac{4}{\boxed{}} = \dfrac{\boxed{}}{30}$

b. $\dfrac{2}{3} = \dfrac{\boxed{}}{9} = \dfrac{10}{\boxed{}}$

c. $\dfrac{5}{8} = \dfrac{\boxed{}}{24} = \dfrac{25}{\boxed{}}$

d. $\dfrac{4}{7} = \dfrac{\boxed{}}{42} = \dfrac{32}{\boxed{}}$

SRB 108 109

---

2. Write *true* or *false* for each number sentence.

a. $5 * (6 + 3) = (5 * 6) + (5 * 3)$ _____

b. $(2 * 10^2) + (1 * 10^1) + (6 * 10^0)$

   $= 2{,}160$ _____

c. $\dfrac{1}{2} + \dfrac{5}{6} + \dfrac{1}{3} = \dfrac{1}{3} + \dfrac{1}{2} + \dfrac{5}{6}$ _____

d. $16 - (4 + 8 - 2) / 2 = 3$ _____

e. $10^6 = 1$ billion _____

SRB 222 223

---

3. On the grid, draw each animal whose location is given below.

a. A bird in C2.

b. A fish in D6.

c. A turtle in E3.

d. A snake in F1.

e. A frog in F4.

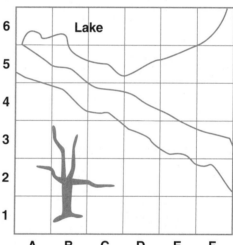

SRB 208

---

4. Draw an isosceles triangle.

Write a definition of an isosceles triangle.

_____

_____

_____

_____

_____

_____

SRB 144

---

5. The shapes below represent geometric solids. Name the solids.

a. _____   b. _____

SRB 147–149

LESSON 8·8   Review Converting Fractions to Mixed Numbers

Math Message

You know that fractions larger than 1 can be written in several ways.

Whole
hexagon

Example:

If a ⬡ is worth 1,

what is ⬡⬡⬡⬡ worth?

The mixed-number name is $3\frac{5}{6}$ ($3\frac{5}{6}$ means $3 + \frac{5}{6}$).

The fraction name is $\frac{23}{6}$. Think *sixths:*

$3\frac{5}{6}$, $3 + \frac{5}{6}$, and $\frac{23}{6}$ are different names for the same number.

Write the following mixed numbers as fractions.

1. $2\frac{3}{5}$ = _____

2. $4\frac{7}{8}$ = _____

3. $1\frac{2}{3}$ = _____

4. $3\frac{6}{4}$ = _____

Write the following fractions as mixed or whole numbers.

5. $\frac{7}{3}$ = _____

6. $\frac{6}{1}$ = _____

7. $\frac{18}{4}$ = _____

8. $\frac{9}{3}$ = _____

Add.

9. $2 + \frac{7}{8}$ = _____

10. $1 + \frac{3}{4}$ = _____

11. $3 + \frac{3}{5}$ = _____

12. $6 + 2\frac{1}{3}$ = _____

Number Sense 1.0; Number Sense 2.3

LESSON 8·8 — Multiplying Fractions and Mixed Numbers

Using Partial Products

Example 1:

$$2\frac{1}{3} * 2\frac{1}{2} = (2 + \frac{1}{3}) * (2 + \frac{1}{2})$$

$$2 * 2 = \quad 4$$

$$2 * \frac{1}{2} = \quad 1$$

$$\frac{1}{3} * 2 = \quad \frac{2}{3}$$

$$\frac{1}{3} * \frac{1}{2} = +\frac{1}{6}$$

$$\overline{\quad 5\frac{5}{6}}$$

Example 2:

$$3\frac{1}{4} * \frac{2}{5} = (3 + \frac{1}{4}) * \frac{2}{5}$$

$$3 * \frac{2}{5} = \frac{6}{5} = \quad 1\frac{1}{5}$$

$$\frac{1}{4} * \frac{2}{5} = \frac{2}{20} = \quad +\frac{1}{10}$$

$$\overline{\quad 1\frac{3}{10}}$$

Converting Mixed Numbers to Fractions

Example 3:

$$2\frac{1}{3} * 2\frac{1}{2} = \frac{7}{3} * \frac{5}{2}$$

$$= \frac{35}{6} = 5\frac{5}{6}$$

Example 4:

$$3\frac{1}{4} * \frac{2}{5} = \frac{13}{4} * \frac{2}{5}$$

$$= \frac{26}{20} = 1\frac{6}{20} = 1\frac{3}{10}$$

Solve the following fraction and mixed-number multiplication problems.

1. $3\frac{1}{2} * 2\frac{1}{5} =$ _____

2. $10\frac{3}{4} * \frac{1}{2} =$ _____

3. The back face of a calculator has an area of about

_____ in².

$5\frac{5}{8}$"

$2\frac{7}{8}$"

4. The area of this sheet of notebook paper is about

_____ in².

10$\frac{1}{2}$"

8"

5. The area of this computer disk is about

_____ in².

$3\frac{5}{6}$"

$3\frac{1}{2}$"

6. The area of this flag is about

_____ yd².

$2\frac{1}{3}$ yd

$3\frac{3}{5}$ yd

7. Is the flag's area greater or less than that of your desk? _____

Number Sense 2.4, 2.5

LESSON 8·8 Track Records on the Moon and the Planets

Every moon and planet in our solar system pulls objects toward it with a force called **gravity.**

In a recent Olympic games, the winning high jump was 7 feet 8 inches, or $7\frac{2}{3}$ feet. The winning pole vault was 19 feet. Suppose that the Olympics were held on Earth's Moon, or on Jupiter, Mars, or Venus. What height might we expect for a winning high jump or a winning pole vault?

1. On the Moon, one could jump about 6 times as high as on Earth. What would be the height of the winning …

   high jump? About _____ feet   pole vault? About _____ feet

2. On Jupiter, one could jump about $\frac{3}{8}$ as high as on Earth. What would be the height of the winning …

   high jump? About _____ feet   pole vault? About _____ feet

3. On Mars, one could jump about $2\frac{2}{3}$ times as high as on Earth. What would be the height of the winning …

   high jump? About _____ feet   pole vault? About _____ feet

4. On Venus, one could jump about $1\frac{1}{7}$ times as high as on Earth. What would be the height of the winning …

   high jump? About _____ feet   pole vault? About _____ feet

5. Is Jupiter's pull of gravity stronger or weaker than Earth's? Explain your reasoning.

   _____

   _____

   _____

Try This

6. The winning pole-vault height given above was rounded to the nearest whole number. The actual winning height was 19 feet $\frac{1}{4}$ inch. If you used this actual measurement, about how many feet high would the winning jump be …

   on the Moon? _____   on Jupiter? _____

   on Mars? _____   on Venus? _____

Number Sense 2.4, 2.5

LESSON 8·8 Finding Fractions of a Number

One way to find a fraction of a number is to use a **unit fraction.** A unit fraction is a fraction with 1 in the numerator. You can also use a diagram to help you understand the problem.

Example: What is $\frac{7}{8}$ of 32?

$\frac{1}{8}$ of 32 is 4. So $\frac{7}{8}$ of 32 is 7 * 4 = 28.

Solve.

1. $\frac{1}{5}$ of 75 = _____

2. $\frac{2}{5}$ of 75 = _____

3. $\frac{4}{5}$ of 75 = _____

4. $\frac{1}{8}$ of 120 = _____

5. $\frac{3}{8}$ of 120 = _____

6. $\frac{5}{8}$ of 120 = _____

Solve Problems 7–18. They come from a math book that was published in 1904.

First think of $\frac{1}{3}$ of each of these numbers, and then state $\frac{2}{3}$ of each.

7. 9 _____

8. 6 _____

9. 12 _____

10. 3 _____

11. 21 _____

12. 30 _____

First think of $\frac{1}{4}$ of each of these numbers, and then state $\frac{3}{4}$ of each.

13. 32 _____

14. 40 _____

15. 12 _____

16. 24 _____

17. 20 _____

18. 28 _____

19. Lydia has 7 pages of a 12-page song memorized. Has she memorized more than $\frac{2}{3}$ of the song? _____

20. A CD that normally sells for $15 is on sale for $\frac{1}{3}$ off. What is the sale price? _____

21. Christine bought a coat for $\frac{1}{4}$ off the regular price. She saved $20. What did she pay for the coat? _____

22. Seri bought 12 avocados on sale for $8.28. What is the unit price, the cost for 1 avocado?

_____

Number Sense 2.5

LESSON 8·8 **Math Boxes**

---

1. a. Write a 7-digit numeral that has

5 in the ten-thousands place,
6 in the tens place,
9 in the ones place,
7 in the hundreds place,
3 in the hundredths place, and
2 in all the other places. _____

b. Write this numeral in expanded notation.

_____

SRB
4

---

2. Write 3 equivalent fractions for each number.

a. $\frac{2}{7}$ _____

b. $\frac{3}{5}$ _____

c. $\frac{5}{8}$ _____

d. $\frac{20}{30}$ _____

e. $\frac{25}{50}$ _____

SRB
59

---

3. Ellen played her guitar $2\frac{1}{3}$ hours on Saturday and $1\frac{1}{4}$ hours on Sunday. How much longer did she play on Saturday?

Number model: _____

Answer: _____

SRB
71

---

4. Complete.

a. $\frac{8}{20} = \frac{\boxed{}}{5}$

b. $\frac{4}{50} = \frac{\boxed{}}{25}$

c. $\frac{6}{20} = \frac{3}{\boxed{}}$

d. $\frac{2}{18} = \frac{1}{\boxed{}}$

SRB
108 109

---

5. Use your Geometry Template to draw a scalene triangle.

How does the scalene triangle differ from other triangles on the Geometry Template?

_____

_____

SRB
134

---

1) MR 2.4   2) NS 2.4   3) NS 2.3
4) NS 2.4   5) MG 2.1

LESSON 8·9 Finding a Percent of a Number

1. The Madison Middle School boys' basketball team has played 5 games. The table at the right shows the number of shots taken by each player and the percent of shots that were baskets. Study the example. Then calculate the number of baskets made by each player.

Example:

Bill took 15 shots.
He made a basket on 40% of these shots.

$$40\% = \frac{40}{100}, \text{ or } \frac{4}{10}$$

$$\frac{4}{10} \text{ of } 15 = \frac{4}{10} * \frac{15}{1} = \frac{4 * 15}{10 * 1} = \frac{60}{10} = 6$$

Bill made 6 baskets.

Player	Shots Taken	Percent Made	Baskets
Bill	15	40%	6
Amit	40	30%	
Josh	25	60%	
Kevin	8	75%	
Mike	60	25%	
Zheng	44	25%	
André	50	10%	
David	25	20%	
Bob	18	50%	
Lars	15	20%	
Justin	28	25%	

2. On the basis of shooting ability, which five players would you select as the starting lineup for the next basketball game?

_____

Explain your choices.

_____

_____

3. Which player(s) would you encourage to shoot more often? _____

Why? _____

_____

4. Which player(s) would you encourage to pass more often? _____

Why? _____

_____

LESSON 8·9

Calculating a Discount

Example: The list price for a toaster is $45. The toaster is sold at a 12% discount (12% off the list price). What are the savings? (***Reminder:*** $12\% = \frac{12}{100} = 0.12$)

Paper and pencil:

$$12\% \text{ of } \$45 \quad = \frac{12}{100} * 45 = \frac{12}{100} * \frac{45}{1}$$

$$= \frac{12 * 45}{100 * 1} = \frac{540}{100}$$

$$= \$5.40$$

Calculator A: Enter 0.12 ⊗ 45 (Enter) and interpret the answer of 5.4 as $5.40.

Calculator B: Enter 0.12 ⊗ 45 (=) and interpret the answer of 5.4 as $5.40.

First use your percent sense to estimate the discount for each item in the table below. The **discount** is the amount by which the list price of an item is reduced. It is the amount the customer saves.

Then use your calculator or paper and pencil to calculate the discount.
(If necessary, round to the nearest cent.)

Item	List Price	Percent of Discount	Estimated Discount	Calculated Discount
Clock radio	$33.00	20%		
Calculator	$60.00	7%		
Sweater	$20.00	42%		
Tent	$180.00	30%		
Bicycle	$200.00	17%		
Computer	$980.00	25%		
Skis	$325.00	18%		
Double CD	$29.99	15%		
Jacket	$110.00	55%		

Number Sense **1.2**; Mathematical Reasoning 2.0

LESSON 8·9 Math Boxes

1. Rename each fraction as a mixed number or a whole number.

a. $\frac{79}{8} =$ _____

b. $\frac{45}{9} =$ _____

c. $\frac{111}{3} =$ _____

d. $\frac{126}{6} =$ _____

e. $\frac{108}{5} =$ _____

SRB 62

2. Find the area of the rectangle.

Number model: _____

_____

_____

Answer: _____

SRB 189

3. Sam has 8 pounds of oats. A cup of oats is about $\frac{1}{2}$ a pound. How many cups of oats does Sam have?

_____

SRB 79 80

4. Julie makes $4.00 per week for washing dishes. She pays her sister Amy $0.75 each time Amy does the dishes for her. Is that fair? Explain.

_____

_____

_____

_____

SRB 42

5. a. Plot the following points on the grid:
(4,2); (2,4); (2,7); (6,7)

b. Connect the points with line segments in the order given above. Then connect (6,7) and (4,2). What shape have you drawn?

_____

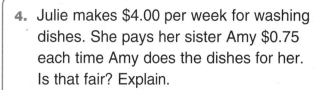

SRB 208

LESSON 8·10 — Unit Fractions and Unit Percents

Math Message

1.

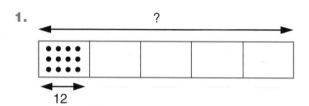

? (top arrow)

12 (bottom arrow)

If 12 counters are $\frac{1}{5}$ of a set,
how many counters are in the set?   _____ counters

2. If 15 counters are $\frac{1}{7}$ of a set,
how many counters are in the set?   _____ counters

3. Complete the diagram in Problem 1 to show your answer.

4. If 31 pages are $\frac{1}{8}$ of a book,
how many pages are in the book?

Number model: _____

Answer: _____ pages

5. If 13 marbles are 1% of the marbles
in a jar, how many marbles are in
the jar?

Number model: _____

Answer: _____ marbles

6. If $5.43 is 1% of the cost of a TV,
how much does the TV cost?

Number model: _____

Answer: _____ dollars

7. If 84 counters are 10% of a set,
how many counters are in the set?

Number model: _____

Answer: _____ counters

8. After 80 minutes, Dorothy had read
120 pages of a 300-page book. If she
continues reading at the same rate,
about how long will it take her to
read the entire book?

Number model: _____

Answer: _____ min

9. Eighty-four people attended a school
concert. This was 70% of the number
expected to attend. How many people
were expected to attend?

Number model: _____

Answer: _____ people

Number Sense **1.2**, 2.4, 2.5; Algebra and Functions **1.2**

LESSON 8·10 Using Units to Find the Whole

1. Six jars are filled with buttons. The number of buttons in each jar is not known. For each clue given below, find the number of buttons in the jar.

	Clue	Number of buttons in Jar
a.	$\frac{1}{2}$ jar contains 31 buttons.	
b.	$\frac{3}{5}$ jar contains 36 buttons.	
c.	$\frac{2}{8}$ jar contains 10 buttons.	
d.	$\frac{3}{8}$ jar contains 21 buttons.	
e.	$\frac{4}{7}$ jar contains 64 buttons.	
f.	$\frac{3}{11}$ jar contains 45 buttons.	

2. Use your percent sense to estimate the list price for each item. Then calculate the list price.

Sale Price	Percent of List Price	Estimated List Price	Calculated List Price
$120.00	60%	$180.00	$200.00
$100.00	50%		
$255.00	85%		
$450.00	90%		

3. Use the given rule to complete the table.

Rule

out = 25% of in

in	out
44	
	25
64	
	31
304	
116	

4. Find the rule. Then complete the table.

Rule

out = ____% of in

in	out
100	40
45	18
60	24
	32
	16
125	

LESSON 8·10   Using Units to Find the WHOLE *continued*

5. Alan is walking to a friend's house. He covered $\frac{6}{10}$ of the distance in 48 minutes. If he continues at the same speed, about how long will the entire walk take? _____

6. 27 is $\frac{3}{4}$ of what number? _____

7. $\frac{3}{8}$ is $\frac{3}{4}$ of what number? _____

8. 16 is 25% of what number? _____

9. 40 is 80% of what number? _____

The problems below are from an arithmetic book published in 1906. Solve the problems.

10. If the average coal miner works $\frac{2}{3}$ of a month with 30 days, how many days during the month does he work? _____ days

11. A recipe for fudge calls for $\frac{1}{4}$ of a cake of chocolate. If a cake costs 20¢, find the cost of the chocolate cake called for by the recipe. _____ ¢

12. A collection of mail that required 6 hours for a postman to make with a horse and wagon was made in an automobile in $\frac{5}{12}$ the time. How long did the automobile take?

_____ hours

13. How many corks per day does a machine in Spain make from the bark of a cork tree if it makes $\frac{1}{3}$ of a sack of 15,000 corks in that time?

_____ corks

Source: *Milne's Progressive Arithmetic*

14. Alice had a jar of buttons. 24 buttons are 40% of the total in the jar. Complete the table showing the number of buttons for each percent.

%	10%	20%	30%	40%	50%	60%	70%	80%	90%	100%
Buttons				24						

15. Explain how you found 100% or the total number of buttons Alice had.

_____

_____

_____

_____

Number Sense **1.2**, 2.5; Algebra and Functions 1.0; Mathematical Reasoning 2.0

LESSON 8·10 **Math Boxes**

---

1. Solve the following problems.

   a. If there are 6 counters in $\frac{1}{2}$ of a set, how many are there in the whole set?

     _____ counters

   b. 9 counters in $\frac{3}{4}$ of a set. How many are there in the whole set?

     _____ counters

   c. 15 counters in the whole set. How many are there in $\frac{2}{3}$ of the set?

     _____ counters

SRB 74 75

---

2. Complete the table.

Fraction	Decimal	Percent
$\frac{3}{5}$		
		5%
	0.70	
$\frac{1}{3}$		
	0.625	

SRB 89 90

---

3. Add.

   a. $3\frac{1}{8} + 2\frac{1}{4} =$ _____

   b. _____ $= 5\frac{3}{5} + 4\frac{3}{5}$

   c. _____ $= 1\frac{7}{8} + 2\frac{1}{2}$

   d. _____ $= \frac{8}{10} + 3\frac{5}{4}$

   e. _____ $= \frac{7}{8} + \frac{1}{5}$

SRB 70

---

4. Grace ran 40 m in 8 seconds. At that speed, how far did she run in 1 second?

_____

SRB 21 108 109

---

5. Complete.

   a. $\frac{1}{2}$ hour = _____ minutes

   b. $\frac{2}{6}$ hour = _____ minutes

   c. $1\frac{1}{2}$ hours = _____ minutes

   d. $3\frac{1}{2}$ days = _____ hours

   e. 2 years = _____ weeks

SRB 397

---

6. Measure line segment *IT* below to the nearest tenth of a centimeter.

_____
I   *T*

IT is about _____ cm.

SRB 183

LESSON 8·11   Class Survey

1. How many people live in your home?

   ◯ 1–2 people   ◯ 3–5 people   ◯ 6 or more people

2. What language do you speak at home?

   ◯ English   ◯ Spanish   ◯ Other: _____

3. Are you right-handed or left-handed?

   ◯ right-handed   ◯ left-handed

4. How long have you lived at your current address? (Round to the nearest year.)

   _____ years

5. Pick one of the questions above. Tell why someone you don't know might be interested in your answer to the question you picked.

   _____

   _____

   _____

   _____

   _____

6. Fifteen percent of the 20 students in Ms. Swanson's class were left-handed.

   How many students were left-handed? _____ students

7. About 85% of the 600 students at Emerson Middle School speak English at home. Another 10% speak Spanish, and 5% speak other languages. About how many students speak each language at home?

   English: _____ students

   Spanish: _____ students

   Other: _____ students

8. The government reported that about 5% of 148,000,000 workers do not have jobs.

   How many workers were jobless? _____ workers

Number Sense 1.2; Statistics, Data Analysis, and Probability 1.3

LESSON 8·11 Rural and Urban Populations

The U.S. Census Bureau classifies where people live according to the
following rule: **Rural** areas are communities having fewer than 2,500 people
each. **Urban** areas are communities having 2,500 or more people each.

1. According to the Census Bureau's definition, do you live in a rural or an urban area?

_____

How did you decide? _____

_____

_____

Today more than three out of every four residents in the United States live in areas
the Census Bureau defines as urban. This was not always the case. When the
United States was formed, it was a rural nation.

Work with your classmates and use the information in the *Student Reference Book,*
pages 350, 351, and 376 to examine the transformation of the United States from a
rural to an urban nation.

2. My group is to estimate the number of people living in _____ areas in

    _____.
    (1790, 1850, 1900, or 2000)
    ̲(̲r̲u̲r̲a̲l̲ ̲o̲r̲ ̲u̲r̲b̲a̲n̲)

3. The total U.S. population in _____ was _____.
    (1790, 1850, 1900, or 2000)

4. Estimate: The number of people living in _____ areas in
    ̲(̲r̲u̲r̲a̲l̲ ̲o̲r̲ ̲u̲r̲b̲a̲n̲)
    _____ was about _____.
    (1790, 1850, 1900, or 2000)
    Make sure your answer is rounded to the nearest 100,000.

5. Our estimation strategy was _____

_____

_____

_____

Number Sense 1.1; Mathematical Reasoning 2.1

LESSON 8·11 **Rural and Urban Populations** *continued*

6. Use the estimates from the groups in your class to complete the following table.

Estimated Rural and Urban Populations, 1790–2000		
Year	Estimated Rural Population	Estimated Urban Population
1790		
1850		
1900		
2000		

7. Is it fair to say that for more than half our nation's history, the **majority** of the population lived in rural areas?

Explain your answer.

Vocabulary
majority means *more than one-half of a count*

_____

_____

_____

_____

8. About how many times larger was the rural population in 2000 than in 1790?

_____

9. About how many times larger was the urban population in 2000 than in 1790?

_____

10. In which decade do you think the urban population became larger than the rural population?

_____

_____

Number Sense 1.1; Mathematical Reasoning 2.1

LESSON 8·11 Math Boxes

---

1. Rename each fraction as a mixed number or a whole number.

a. $\dfrac{36}{8} =$ _____

b. $\dfrac{36}{7} =$ _____

c. $\dfrac{99}{13} =$ _____

d. $\dfrac{13}{7} =$ _____

e. $\dfrac{18}{6} =$ _____

SRB
62

---

2. Find the area of the rectangle.

Number model: _____

_____

_____

Answer: _____

SRB
189

---

3. Rico is ordering 12 pizzas. How many people can Rico serve if each person eats $\dfrac{1}{4}$ of a pizza?

_____

SRB
79 80

---

4. Fran has $6.48. She buys a hamburger for $2.83. How much does she have left?

_____

Number model: _____

Explain your answer.

_____

_____

_____

SRB
34

---

5. Plot the following points on the grid:

(0,1); (1,3); (4,3); (5,1)

Connect the points with line segments in the given order. Then connect (5,1) and (0,1). What shape have you drawn?

_____

_____

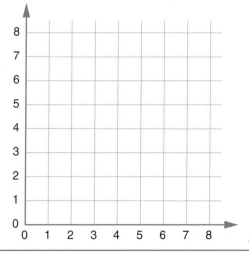

SRB
208

LESSON 8·12 Division

Math Message

1. How many 2-pound boxes of candy can be made from 10 pounds of candy?

   _____ boxes

2. How many $\frac{1}{2}$-pound boxes of candy can be made from 6 pounds of candy?

   _____ boxes

3. Sam has 5 pounds of peanut brittle. He wants to pack it in $\frac{3}{4}$-pound packages.

   How many full packages can he make? _____ full packages

   Will any peanut brittle be left over? _____ How much? _____ pound

4.

   a. How many 2-inch segments are in 6 inches? _____ segments

   b. How many $\frac{1}{2}$-inch segments are in 6 inches? _____ segments

   c. How many $\frac{1}{8}$-inch segments are in $\frac{3}{4}$ of an inch? _____ segments

Common Denominator Division

One way to divide fractions uses common denominators.

Step 1 Rename the fractions using a common denominator.
Step 2 Divide the numerators.

This method can also be used for whole or mixed numbers divided by fractions.

Examples:

$$3 \div \frac{3}{4} = ?$$
$$3 \div \frac{3}{4} = \frac{12}{4} \div \frac{3}{4}$$
$$= 12 \div 3 = 4$$

$$\frac{1}{3} \div \frac{1}{6} = ?$$
$$\frac{1}{3} \div \frac{1}{6} = \frac{2}{6} \div \frac{1}{6}$$
$$= 2 \div 1 = 2$$

$$3\frac{3}{5} \div \frac{3}{5} = \frac{18}{5} \div \frac{3}{5}$$
$$= 18 \div 3 = 6$$

Number Sense 2.4, 2.5

Date _____ Time _____

Solve.

1. $4 \div \frac{4}{5} =$ _____

2. $\frac{5}{6} \div \frac{1}{18} =$ _____

3. $3\frac{1}{3} \div \frac{5}{6} =$ _____

4. $6\frac{3}{5} \div 2\frac{2}{10} =$ _____

5. $2 \div \frac{2}{5} =$ _____

6. $2 \div \frac{2}{3} =$ _____

7. $6 \div \frac{3}{5} =$ _____

8. $\frac{1}{2} \div \frac{1}{8} =$ _____

9. $\frac{3}{5} \div \frac{1}{10} =$ _____

10. $\frac{6}{5} \div \frac{3}{10} =$ _____

11. $1\frac{1}{2} \div \frac{3}{4} =$ _____

12. $4\frac{1}{5} \div \frac{3}{5} =$ _____

13. Explain how you solved Problem 12. _____

_____

_____

_____

_____

14. Chase is packing cookies in $\frac{1}{2}$-pound bags. He has 10 pounds of cookies.

   How many bags can he pack? _____ bags

15. Regina is cutting lanyard to make bracelets. She has 15 feet of lanyard and needs $1\frac{1}{2}$ feet for each bracelet. How many bracelets can she make?

   _____ bracelets

16. Eric is planning a pizza party. He has 3 large pizzas. He figures each person will eat $\frac{3}{8}$ of a pizza. How many people can attend the party, including himself?

   _____ people

LESSON 8·12 **Math Boxes**

---

1. Find the whole set.

  a. 10 is $\frac{1}{5}$ of the set. _____

  b. 12 is $\frac{3}{4}$ of the set. _____

  c. 8 is $\frac{2}{7}$ of the set. _____

  d. 15 is $\frac{5}{8}$ of the set. _____

  e. 9 is $\frac{3}{5}$ of the set. _____

  SRB 74 75

---

2. Complete the table.

Fraction	Decimal	Percent
$\frac{4}{5}$		
	0.125	
$\frac{11}{20}$		
		$66\frac{2}{3}\%$
	0.857	

  SRB 89 90

---

3. Add.

  a. $2\frac{3}{4} + 1\frac{1}{2} =$ _____

  b. _____ $= \frac{3}{8} + \frac{5}{6}$

  c. $6\frac{1}{5} + 3\frac{2}{3} =$ _____

  d. _____ $= 5\frac{1}{8} + \frac{14}{8}$

  e. _____ $= 4\frac{3}{10} + 6\frac{1}{2}$

  SRB 70

---

4. A worker can fill 145 boxes of crackers in 15 minutes. At that rate, how many can she fill in 1 hour?

  _____

  SRB 19 20 108 109

---

5. Write a fraction or a mixed number for each of the following:

  a. 15 minutes = _____ hour

  b. 40 minutes = _____ hour

  c. 45 minutes = _____ hour

  d. 25 minutes = _____ hour

  e. 12 minutes = _____ hour

  SRB 62 63

---

6. Measure the line segment below to the nearest $\frac{1}{4}$ inch.

  _____

  _____ in.

  SRB 183

---

1) NS 2.5   2) NS 1.2   3) NS 2.3
4) NS 2.5   5) MR 2.2   6) MR 1.0

LESSON 8·13   Math Boxes

---

1. Find the area of the rectangle.

Area = b * h

5 yd

8 yd

Area: _____

SRB 189

---

2. Draw a quadrangle with two pairs of parallel sides.

What kind of quadrangle is this?

_____

SRB 145 146

---

3. Measure the dimensions of your calculator to the nearest $\frac{1}{4}$ inch. Record your measurements on the drawing below.

SRB 183

---

4. A copy machine was used to copy the trapezoid *ABCD*. Are the trapezoids congruent? _____

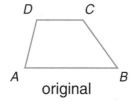

D   C   D   C

A   B   A   B
   original   copy

Explain. _____

_____

_____

_____

SRB 155

---

5. a. Plot the following points on the grid: (2,5); (4,7); (6,5); (4,1)

   b. Connect the points with line segments in the order given above. Then connect (4,1) and (2,5). What shape have you drawn?

   _____

SRB 208

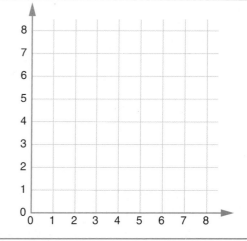

LESSON 9·1   Plotting a Turtle

Points on a coordinate grid are named by ordered number pairs. The first number in an ordered number pair locates the point along the horizontal axis. The second number locates the point along the vertical axis. To mark a point on a coordinate grid, first go right or left on the horizontal axis. Then go up or down from there.

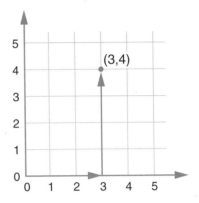

Plot an outline of the turtle on the graph below. Start with the nose, at point (8,12).

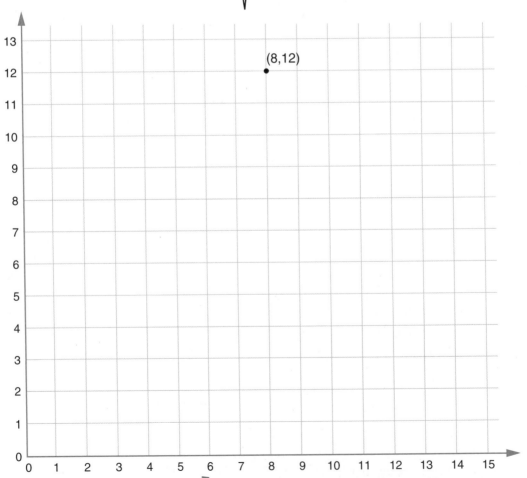

Algebra and Functions **1.4**; Statistics, Data Analysis, and Probability **1.5**

LESSON 9·1   *Hidden Treasure* Gameboards 1

Each player uses Grids 1 and 2.

Grid 1: Hide your point here.

Grid 2: Guess other player's point here.

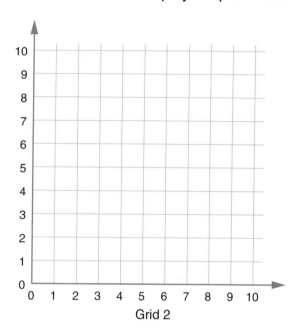

Use this set of grids to play another game.

Grid 1: Hide your point here.

Grid 2: Guess other player's point here.

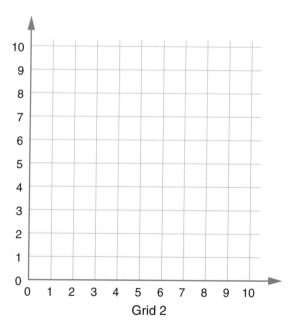

LESSON 9·1

Matching Graphs to Number Stories

1. Draw a line matching each graph below to the number story that it best fits.

a. Juanita started with $350. She saved another $25 every week.

Graph A

b. Meredith received $350 for her birthday. She deposited the entire amount in the bank. Every week, she withdrew $50.

Graph B

c. Julian started a new savings account with $50. Every week after that, he deposited $75.

Graph C

2. Explain how you decided which graph matches each number story.

_____

_____

_____

_____

3. Circle the rule below that best fits the number story in Problem 1a above.

Savings = $350 + (25 * number of weeks)

Savings = $350 − (25 * number of weeks)

Savings = $350 * number of weeks

Algebra and Functions **1.5**; Statistics, Data Analysis, and Probability **1.4**

LESSON 9·1   **Math Boxes**

---

1. Draw a circle with a radius of 2 centimeters.

What is the diameter of the circle? _____
(unit)

SRB
153 162

---

2. Multiply.

a. $\dfrac{3}{8} * \dfrac{4}{7} =$ _____

b. $1\dfrac{1}{8} * 2\dfrac{3}{4} =$ _____

c. $2\dfrac{2}{3} * 1\dfrac{3}{5} =$ _____

d. $2\dfrac{1}{6} * 3\dfrac{1}{4} =$ _____

SRB
77

---

3. What is the volume of the rectangular prism? Circle the best answer.

A 32 units^3

B 160 units^3

C 130 units^3

D 80 units^3

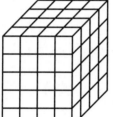

SRB
197

---

4. If you picked a number at random from the grid below, what is the probability that it would be an odd number?

1	2	3	4	5
6	7	8	9	10
11	12	13	14	15

Fraction _____

Percent _____

SRB
128 129

---

5. Write a number sentence to represent the story. Then solve.

Alex earns $8.00 per hour when he babysits. How much will he earn in $4\dfrac{1}{2}$ hours?

Number sentence:

_____

Solution: _____

SRB
219

---

6. Write the prime factorization of each number.

a. 38 = _____

b. 92 = _____

c. 56 = _____

d. 72 = _____

e. 125 = _____

SRB
12

LESSON 9·2 Sailboat Graphs

1. a. Using the ordered number pairs listed in the column titled Original Sailboat in the table below, plot the ordered number pairs on the grid titled Original Sailboat on the next page.

   b. Connect the points in the same order that you plot them. You should see the outline of a sailboat.

2. Fill in the missing coordinates in the last three columns of the table. Use the rule given in each column to calculate the ordered number pairs.

Original Sailboat	New Sailboat 1 Rule: Double each number of the original pair.	New Sailboat 2 Rule: Double the first number of the original pair.	New Sailboat 3 Rule: Double the second number of the original pair.
(8,1)	(16,2)	(16,1)	(8,2)
(5,1)	(10,2)	(10,1)	(5,2)
(5,7)	(10,14)	(10,7)	(5,14)
(1,2)	(____ , ____)	(____ , ____)	(____ , ____)
(5,1)	(____ , ____)	(____ , ____)	(____ , ____)
(0,1)	(____ , ____)	(____ , ____)	(____ , ____)
(2,0)	(____ , ____)	(____ , ____)	(____ , ____)
(7,0)	(____ , ____)	(____ , ____)	(____ , ____)
(8,1)	(____ , ____)	(____ , ____)	(____ , ____)

3. a. Plot the ordered number pairs for New Sailboat 1 on the next page. Connect the points in the same order that you plot them.

   b. Then plot the ordered number pairs for New Sailboat 2, and connect the points.

   c. Finally, plot the ordered number pairs for New Sailboat 3, and connect the points.

Algebra and Functions **1.4**; Statistics, Data Analysis, and Probability **1.5**

Date _____ Time _____

Sailboat Graphs *continued*

Original Sailboat

New Sailboat 1

New Sailboat 2

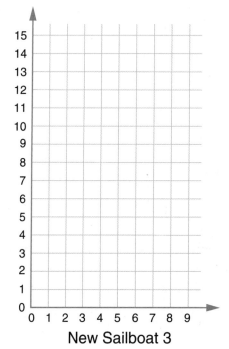

New Sailboat 3

LESSON 9·2

Plotting a Map

1. **a.** Plot the following ordered number pairs on the grid:

   (21,14); (17,11); (17,13); (15,14); (2,16); (1,11);
   (2,8); (3,6); (7.5,5.5); (11,2.5); (12.5,4)

   b. Connect all the points in the same order in which they were plotted. Then connect (12.5,4) to (17.5,5) and (21.5,15.5) to (21,14). When you have finished, you should see an outline map of the continental United States.

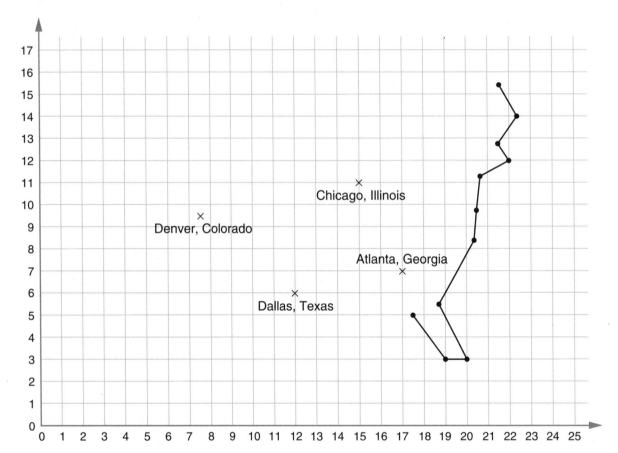

2. Write the coordinates of each city.

   a. Chicago, Illinois (_____ , _____)   **b.** Atlanta, Georgia (_____ , _____)

   c. Dallas, Texas (_____ , _____)   **d.** Denver, Colorado (_____ , _____)

3. Plot each city on the grid and write the city name.

   a. Billings, Montana (7.5,13)   **b.** Salt Lake City, Utah (5.5,10.5)

4. The U.S.–Mexican border is shown by line segments from (3,6) to (7.5,5.5) and from (7.5,5.5) to (11,2.5). Write the border name on the grid.

298

LESSON 9·2   **Math Boxes**

---

1. Write five names for the number 23.

   a. _____

   b. _____

   c. _____

   d. _____

   e. _____

 (SRB 219)

2. What is the volume of the cube below? Choose the best answer.

   ⬭ 32 units^3

   ⬭ 526 units^3

   ⬭ 64 units^3

   ⬭ 256 units^3

(SRB 197)

---

3. Compare. Use <, >, or =.

   a. 3 million _____ 300 thousand

   b. 5^4 _____ 4^5

   c. 2,000 _____ $2 * 10^3$

   d. $9 * 10^3$ _____ 90,000

   e. 10^3 _____ 10 thousand

 (SRB 220 221)

4. Solve.

   a. 75
      *88

   b. 425
      * 68

   c. 759
      * 13

   d. 422
      *185

 (SRB 19 20)

---

5. Write *true* or *false*.

   a. 45,678 is divisible by 2. _____

   b. 34,215 is divisible by 3. _____

   c. 455 is divisible by 5. _____

   d. 4,561 is divisible by 9. _____

 (SRB 11)

6. Complete the "What's My Rule?" table, and state the rule.

   Rule: _____

in	out
5	
3	−2
	5
0	
	−7

 (SRB 231 232)

LESSON 9·3 — More Sailboat Graphs

1. a. Using the ordered number pairs listed in the column titled Original Sailboat in the table below, plot the ordered number pairs on the grid on the next page.

b. Connect the points in the same order that they were plotted. You should see the outline of a sailboat. Write *original* in the sail.

2. Fill in the missing coordinates in the last three columns of the table. Use the rule given in each column to calculate the ordered number pairs.

Original Sailboat	New Sailboat 1 — Rule: Add 10 to the first number of the original pair.	New Sailboat 2 — Rule: Change the first number of the original pair to the opposite number.	New Sailboat 3 — Rule: Change the second number of the original pair to the opposite number.
(9,3)	(19,3)	(−9,3)	(9,−3)
(6,3)	(16,3)	(−6,3)	(6,−3)
(6,9)	(16,9)	(−6,9)	(6,−9)
(2,4)	(_____ , _____)	(_____ , _____)	(_____ , _____)
(6,3)	(_____ , _____)	(_____ , _____)	(_____ , _____)
(1,3)	(_____ , _____)	(_____ , _____)	(_____ , _____)
(3,2)	(_____ , _____)	(_____ , _____)	(_____ , _____)
(8,2)	(_____ , _____)	(_____ , _____)	(_____ , _____)
(9,3)	(_____ , _____)	(_____ , _____)	(_____ , _____)

3. a. Plot the ordered number pairs for New Sailboat 1 on the next page. Connect the points in the same order that you plot them. Write the number 1 in the sail.

b. Then plot the ordered number pairs for New Sailboat 2 and connect the points. Write the number 2 in the sail.

c. Finally, plot the ordered number pairs for New Sailboat 3 and connect the points. Write the number 3 in the sail.

Algebra and Functions **1.4** ; Statistics, Data Analysis, and Probability **1.5**

LESSON
9·3
More Sailboat Graphs *continued*

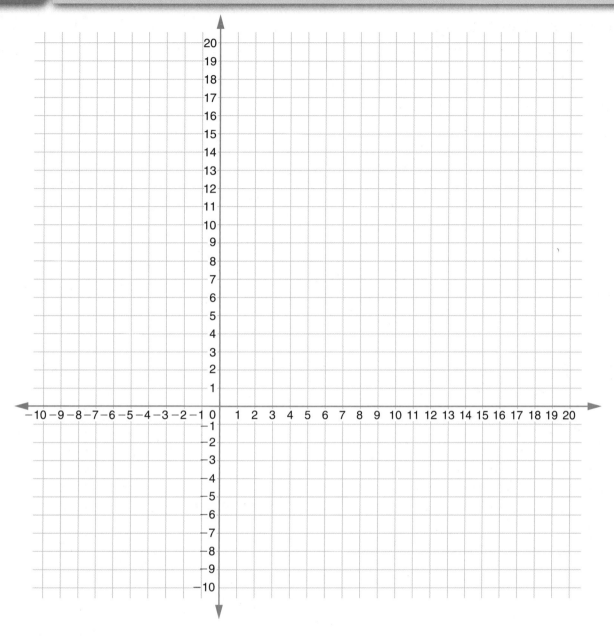

4. Use the following rule to create a new sailboat figure on the coordinate grid above:

   Rule: Add 10 to the second number of the original pair. Leave the first number unchanged.

   Try to plot the new coordinates without listing them. Write the number 4 in the sail.

LESSON 9·3   *Hidden Treasure* Gameboards 2

Each player uses Grids 1 and 2.

Grid 1: Hide your point here.

Grid 2: Guess other player's point here.

Grid 1

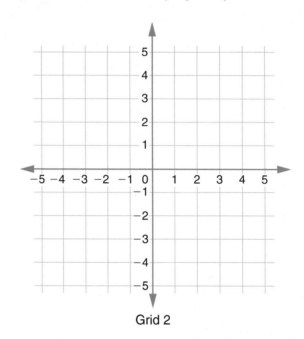

Grid 2

Use this set of grids to play another game.

Grid 1: Hide your point here.

Grid 2: Guess other player's point here.

Grid 1

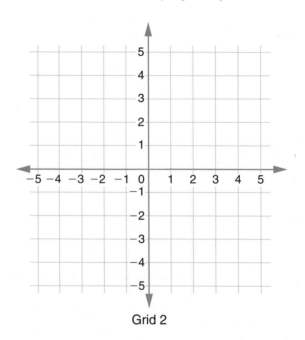

Grid 2

Algebra and Functions **1.4**; Statistics, Data Analysis, and Probability **1.5**

LESSON 9·3   **Math Boxes**

---

1. Draw a circle with a radius of 1 inch. What is the diameter of this circle?

_____
(unit)

153 162

---

2. Multiply.

a. $1\frac{2}{3} * 2\frac{4}{7} =$ _____

b. $1\frac{5}{6} * 4\frac{1}{5} =$ _____

c. _____ $= \frac{7}{8} * \frac{5}{4}$

77

---

3. What is the volume of the rectangular prism? Fill in the circle next to the best answer.

○ **A.** 39 units^3

○ **B.** 15 units^3

○ **C.** 45 units^3

○ **D.** 40 units^3

197

---

4. If you roll a die 60 times, what is the probability you would roll a 1?

Fraction _____

Percent _____

What is the probability you would roll a 1 or 6?

Fraction _____

Percent _____

128 129

---

5. Write a number sentence to represent the story. Then solve.

Carrie is 61 inches tall. Jeff is $3\frac{1}{2}$ inches shorter. How tall is Jeff?

Number sentence: _____

Solution: _____

219

---

1) MG 2.0   2) NS 2.4   3) MG **1·3**
4) NS **1·2**   5) NS **2·3**

LESSON 9·4 Areas of Rectangles

1. Fill in the table. Draw rectangles D, E, and F on the grid.

Rectangle	Base (length)	Height (width)	Area
A	_____ cm	_____ cm	_____ cm²
B	_____ cm	_____ cm	_____ cm²
C	_____ cm	_____ cm	_____ cm²
D	6 cm	_____ cm	12 cm²
E	3.5 cm	_____ cm	14 cm²
F	3 cm	_____ cm	10.5 cm²

2. Write a formula for finding the area of a rectangle.

Area = _____

Measurement and Geometry 1.0, **1.1**, 1.4

Date _____   Time _____

1. A bedroom floor is 12 feet by 15 feet
   (4 yards by 5 yards).

   Floor area = _____ square feet

   Floor area = _____ square yards

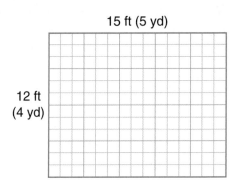

15 ft (5 yd)

12 ft
(4 yd)

2. Imagine that you want to buy carpet for
   the bedroom in Problem 1. The carpet
   comes on a roll that is 6 feet (2 yards)
   wide. The carpet salesperson unrolls the
   carpet to the length you want and cuts
   off your piece. What length of carpet
   will you need to cover the bedroom floor? _____

6 ft
(2 yd)

---

3. Calculate the areas for the
   figures below.

   a.

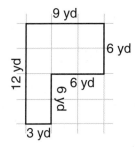

   9 yd
   6 yd
   12 yd
   6 yd
   6 yd
   3 yd

   Area = _____ yd²

   b.

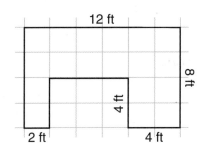

   12 ft
   8 ft
   4 ft
   2 ft   4 ft

   Area = _____ ft²

4. Fill in the missing lengths for
   the figures below.

   a.

   12 ft

   _____ ft   360 ft²   _____ ft

   _____ ft

   b.

   _____ yd

   _____ yd   375 yd²   25 yd

   _____ yd

LESSON 9·4 Review of 2-Dimensional Figures

Match each description of a geometric figure in Column A with its name in Column B.
Not every name in Column B has a match.

A

a. A polygon with 4 right angles and 4 sides of the same length

b. A polygon with 4 sides, no two of which need to be the same size

c. A quadrilateral with exactly one pair of opposite sides that are parallel

d. Lines in the same plane that never intersect

e. A parallelogram (that is not a square) with all sides the same length

f. A polygon with 8 sides

g. Two intersecting lines that form a right angle

h. A polygon with 5 sides

i. An angle that measures 90°

j. A triangle with all sides the same length

B

_____ octagon

_____ rhombus

_____ right angle

_____ acute angle

_____ trapezoid

_____ hexagon

_____ square

_____ equilateral triangle

_____ perpendicular lines

_____ parallel lines

_____ pentagon

_____ isosceles triangle

_____ quadrilateral

Measurement and Geometry 2.0, 2.3

LESSON 9·4 **Math Boxes**

1. Write five names for the number 2.25.

   a. _____

   b. _____

   c. _____

   d. _____

   e. _____

   SRB 219

2. What is volume of the prism? Choose the best answer.

   ◯ 240 units³

   ◯ 90 units²

   ◯ 30 units³

   ◯ 90 units³

   SRB 197

3. Compare. Use <, >, or =.

   a. $8 * 10^5$ _____ 80,000

   b. 12.4 million _____ 12,400,000

   c. 7,000,000 _____ $7 * 10^5$

   d. 8^2 _____ 2^8

   e. $5.4 * 10^2$ _____ 5,400

   SRB 220 221

4. Solve.

   a.   429
       $* 15$

   b.   134
       $* 82$

   c.   706
       $*189$

   SRB 19 20

5. Write *true* or *false*.

   a. 5,278 is divisible by 3. _____

   b. 79,002 is divisible by 6. _____

   c. 86,076 is divisible by 9. _____

   d. 908,321 is divisible by 2. _____

   SRB 11

6. Complete the "What's My Rule?" table, and state the rule.

   Rule: _____

in	out
4	9
7	15
11	23
	19
6	

   SRB 231 232

LESSON 9·5   **Personal References**

Math Message

Personal references are familiar objects whose sizes approximate standard measures. For example, the distance across the tip of many people's smallest finger is about 1 centimeter. You identified personal references for length, weight, and capacity in *Fourth Grade Everyday Mathematics*.

Look around your workspace or classroom to find common objects that have areas of 1 square inch, 1 square foot, 1 square yard, 1 square centimeter, and 1 square meter. The areas do not have to be exact, but they should be reasonable estimates. Work with your group. Try to find more than one reference for each measure.

Unit	My Personal References
1 square inch (1 in^2)	
1 square foot (1 ft^2)	
1 square yard (1 yd^2)	
1 square centimeter (1 cm^2)	
1 square meter (1 m^2)	

Measurement and Geometry **1.1**, 1.4; Mathematical Reasoning 2.3, 3.0

LESSON 9·5 Finding Areas of Nonrectangular Figures

In the previous lesson, you calculated the areas of rectangular figures using two different methods.

◆ You counted the total number of unit squares and parts of unit squares that fit neatly inside the figure.

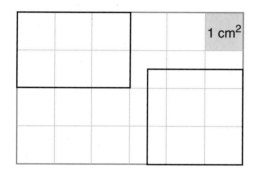

◆ You used the formula $A = b * h$, where the letter A stands for area, the letter b for the length of the base, and the letter h for the height.

However, many times you will need to find the area of a figure that is not a rectangle. Unit squares will not fit neatly inside the figure, and you won't be able to use the formula for the area of a rectangle.

Working with a partner, think of a way to find the area of each of the figures below.

1. What is the area of triangle *ABC*?

_____

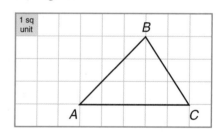

2. What is the area of triangle *XYZ*?

_____

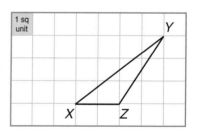

3. What is the area of parallelogram *GRAM*?

_____

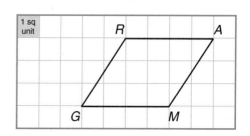

LESSON 9·5 Areas of Triangles and Parallelograms

Use the rectangle method to find the area of each triangle and parallelogram below.

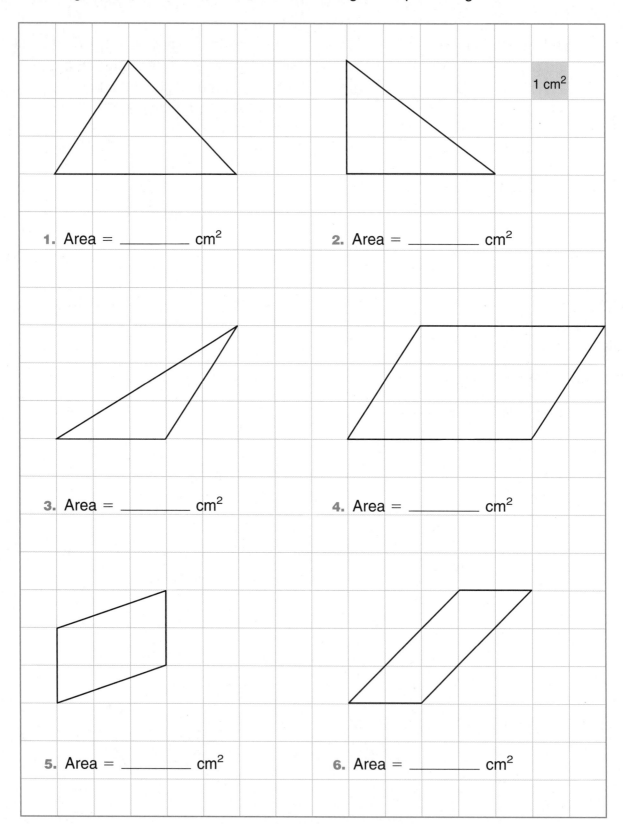

1 cm²

1. Area = _____ cm²

2. Area = _____ cm²

3. Area = _____ cm²

4. Area = _____ cm²

5. Area = _____ cm²

6. Area = _____ cm²

Measurement and Geometry 1.0, 1.1, 1.4; Mathematical Reasoning 3.0, 3.2

LESSON 9·5 **Math Boxes**

---

1. Write the ordered pair for each point on the coordinate grid.

   a. A: (____,____)

   b. B: (____,____)

   c. C: (____,____)

   d. D: (____,____)

   e. E: (____,____)

   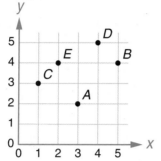

   SRB 208

2. Draw a line segment congruent to line segment *AB*.

   A _____ B

   Explain why the line segments are congruent.

   _____

   _____

   SRB 155

---

3. Complete.

   a. 60 inches = _____ feet

   b. 3 yards = _____ inches

   c. 1 meter = _____ cm

   d. 3,520 yards = _____ miles

   e. 16 mm = _____ cm

   SRB 183 397

4. Write the following numbers in order from least to greatest.

   $\dfrac{9}{2}$ 4.75 $\dfrac{13}{4}$ 4.8 $4\dfrac{7}{8}$

   _____ , _____ , _____ , _____ , _____

   SRB 66 67

---

5. Write a number model that describes each of the shaded rectangles.

   _____   _____   _____

   SRB 219

LESSON 9·6 # Defining *Base* and *Height*

Math Message

Study the figures below. Then write definitions for the words **base** (*b*) and **height** (*h*).

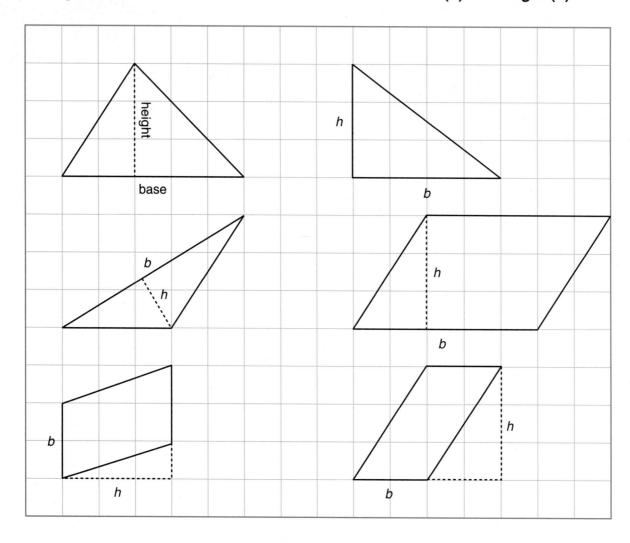

1. Define *base.*

   _____

   _____

   _____

2. Define *height.*

   _____

   _____

   _____

Measurement and Geometry 1.0, **1.1**, 1.4, 2.0

LESSON 9·6 The Rectangle Method

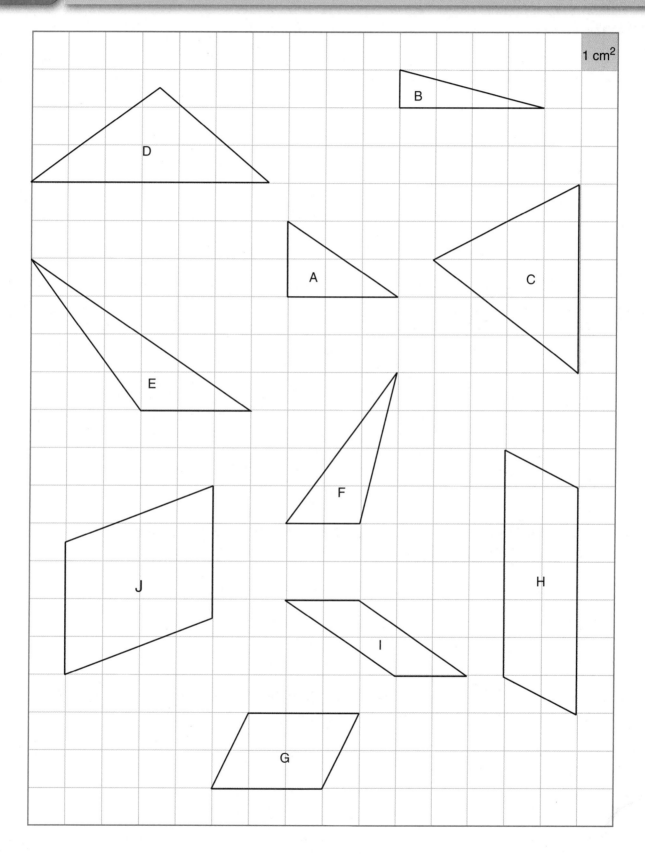

1 cm²

LESSON 9·6

Finding Areas of Triangles and Parallelograms

1. Fill in the table. All figures are shown on journal page 313.

Triangles	Area	base	height	base * height
A	3 cm²	3 cm	2 cm	6 cm²
B	_____ cm²	_____ cm	_____ cm	_____ cm²
C	_____ cm²	_____ cm	_____ cm	_____ cm²
D	_____ cm²	_____ cm	_____ cm	_____ cm²
E	_____ cm²	3 cm	4 cm	_____ cm²
F	_____ cm²	_____ cm	_____ cm	_____ cm²
Parallelograms	**Area**	**base**	**height**	**base * height**
G	6 cm²	3 cm	2 cm	6 cm²
H	_____ cm²	_____ cm	_____ cm	_____ cm²
I	_____ cm²	_____ cm	2 cm	_____ cm²
J	_____ cm²	_____ cm	_____ cm	_____ cm²

2. Examine the results of Figures A–F. Propose a formula for the area of a triangle as an equation and as a word sentence.

   Area of a triangle = _____

   _____

   _____

3. Examine the results of Figures G–J. Propose a formula for the area of a parallelogram as an equation and as a word sentence.

   Area of a parallelogram = _____

   _____

   _____

Measurement and Geometry 1.0, 1.1, 1.4; Mathematical Reasoning 3.2

Date _____   Time _____

1. a. Plot the following points on the grid:

$(-3,-3)$; $(1,1)$; $(4,1)$; $(0,-3)$

b. Connect the points with line segments in the order given above. Then connect $(-3,-3)$ and $(0,-3)$.

What shape have you drawn?

_____

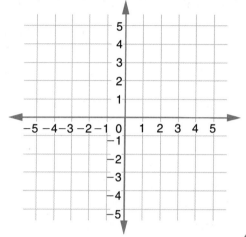

SRB
208

---

2. Find the diameter of the circle. Choose the best answer.

⬭ 4.5 units

⬭ 5 units

⬭ 25 units

⬭ 6 units

2.5 units

SRB
153

---

3. What transformation does the figure below show? Circle the best answer.

A reflection

B translation

C rotation

D dilation

preimage   image

SRB
157 158

---

4. a. What is the perimeter of the rectangle?

_____

12 units

8 units

b. What is the area of the rectangle?

_____

SRB
186

---

5. Complete the "What's My Rule?" table, and state the rule.

Rule: _____

in	out
5	20
4	
6	24
8	

SRB
231 232

LESSON 9·7   Earth's Water Surface

Math Message

1. **a.** What percent of Earth's surface do you think is covered by water?

   My estimate: _____

   b. Explain how you made your estimate.

   _____

   _____

   _____

A Sampling Experiment

2. **a.** My location is at latitude _____ and longitude _____.

   b. Circle one.

   My location is on: land   water

   c. What fraction of the class has a water location? _____

   d. Percent of Earth's Surface that is covered by water:

   My class's estimate: _____

Follow-Up

3. **a.** Percent of Earth's surface that is covered by water:

   Actual figure: _____

   b. How does your class estimate compare to the actual figure?

   _____

   _____

   _____

LESSON 9·7 The Four-4s Problem

Using only four 4s and any operation on your calculator, create expressions for values from 1 through 100. Do not use any other numbers except the ones listed in the rules below. You do not need to find an expression for every number. Some are quite difficult. Try to find as many as you can today, but keep working when you have free time. The rules are listed below:

◆ You must use four 4s in every expression.

◆ You can use two 4s to create 44 or $\frac{4}{4}$.

◆ You may use 4^0 ($4^0 = 1$).

◆ You may use $\sqrt{4}$ ($\sqrt{4} = 2$).

◆ You may use 4! (four factorial). ($4! = 4 * 3 * 2 * 1 = 24$)

◆ You may use the decimal 0.4.

Use parentheses as needed so that it is very clear what is to be done and in what order. Examples of expressions for some numbers are shown below.

1 = _____   16 = _____

2 = _____   17 = _____

3 = _____   18 = _____

4 = _____   19 = _____

5 = _____   20 = _____

6 = _____   21 = _____

7 = _____   22 = _____

8 = _____   23 = _____

$9 = 4 + \sqrt{4} + \sqrt{4} + 4^0$ 24 = _____

10 = _____   25 = _____

11 = _____ $26 = (4! + \sqrt{4}) * \frac{4}{4}$

12 = _____   27 = _____

13 = _____   28 = _____

14 = _____   29 = _____

15 = _____   30 = _____

LESSON 9·7

The Four-4s Problem *continued*

31 = _____

32 = _____

33 = _____

34 = _____

35 = _____

36 = _____

37 = _____

38 = _____

39 = _____

40 = _____

41 = _____

42 = _____

43 = _____

44 = _____

45 = _____

46 = _____

47 = _____

48 = _____

49 = _____

50 = _____

51 = _____

52 = _____

53 = _____

54 = _____

55 = _____

56 = _____

57 = _____

58 = $(\sqrt{4} * (4! + 4)) + \sqrt{4}$

59 = _____

60 = _____

61 = _____

62 = _____

63 = _____

64 = _____

65 = _____

66 = _____

67 = _____

68 = _____

69 = _____

70 = _____

71 = _____

72 = _____

73 = _____

74 = _____

75 = _____

76 = _____

77 = _____

78 = _____

79 = _____

80 = _____

81 = _____

82 = _____

Number Sense 1.1; Mathematical Reasoning 2.0

LESSON 9·7   The Four-4s Problem *continued*

83 = _____   92 = _____

84 = _____   93 = _____

85 = _____   94 = _____

86 = _____   95 = _____

87 = _____   96 = _____

88 = _____   97 = _____

89 = _____   98 = _____

90 = _____   99 = _____

91 = _____   100 = _____

Try This

Using only six 6s and any operation on your calculator, create expressions for values from 1 to 25.

1 = _____   14 = _____

2 = _____   15 = _____

3 = _____   16 = _____

4 = $(6 + 6) \div ((6 + 6 + 6) \div 6)$ 17 = _____

5 = _____   18 = _____

6 = _____   19 = _____

7 = _____   20 = _____

8 = _____   21 = _____

9 = _____   22 = _____

10 = _____   23 = _____

11 = _____   24 = _____

12 = _____   25 = _____

13 = _____

LESSON 9·7 **Math Boxes**

---

1. Write the ordered pairs for each point on the coordinate grid.

a. *A*: (____,____)

b. *B*: (____,____)

c. *C*: (____,____)

d. *D*: (____,____)

e. *E*: (____,____)

SRB 208

---

2. Draw a figure that is congruent to Figure *A*.

Figure A

SRB 155

---

3. Complete.

a. 1.5 km = _____ m

b. 40 in. = _____ yd _____ in.

c. 3 m = _____ mm

d. 5 dm = _____ cm

e. 6 yds = _____ ft

SRB 183 397

---

4. Write the following numbers in order from least to greatest.

$$5.03 \qquad 4\frac{7}{4} \qquad 5.3 \qquad \frac{3}{15} \qquad 5\frac{2}{5}$$

_____, _____, _____, _____, _____

SRB 32 33 66 67

---

5. Write a number model that describes each of the shaded rectangles.

a.

b.

c.

_____   _____   _____

SRB 219

---

1) SDAP 1.4   2) MG 1.4   3) MR 1.0
4) NS 1.5   5) MR 2.3

LESSON 9·8 Rectangular Prisms

A **rectangular prism** is a geometric solid enclosed by six flat surfaces formed by rectangles. If each of the six rectangles is also a square, then the prism is a **cube.** The flat surfaces are called **faces** of the prism.

Bricks, paperback books, and most boxes are rectangular prisms. Dice and sugar cubes are examples of cubes.

Below are three different views of the same rectangular prism.

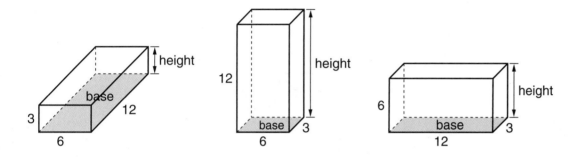

1. Study the figures above. Write your own definitions for **base** and **height.**

   Base of a rectangular prism: _____

   _____

   Height of a rectangular prism: _____

   _____

Examine the patterns on Activity Sheet 6. These patterns will be used to construct open boxes—boxes that have no tops. Try to figure out how many centimeter cubes are needed to fill each box to the top. Do not cut out the patterns yet.

2. I think that _____ centimeter cubes are needed to fill Box A to the top.

3. I think that _____ centimeter cubes are needed to fill Box B to the top.

Date _____   Time _____

Volume of Rectangular Prisms

Write the formula for the volume of a rectangular prism.

_____

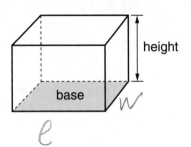

_B_ is the area of the base.

_h_ is the height from that base.

_V_ is the volume of the prism.

$$V = L \cdot W \cdot H$$

Find the volume of each rectangular prism below.

1.

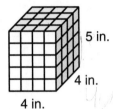

5 in.

4 in.

4 in.

V = ____80 in³____
         (unit)

2.

6 cm

3 cm

4 cm

V = ____72 cm³____
         (unit)

3.

7 cm

7 cm

7 cm

V = ____343 cm³____
         (unit)

4.

4 in.

6 in.

8 in.

V = ____192 in³____
         (unit)

5.

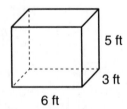

5 ft

3 ft

6 ft

V = ____90 ft³____
         (unit)

6.

5 cm

4 cm

2.5 cm

V = ____50 cm³____
         (unit)

Measurement and Geometry 1.2, 1.3, 1.4

Math Boxes

---

1. Solve.

   a.   128.07
       − 85.25

   b.   306.85
      + 216.96

   c.   18.95
      − 6.07

   d.   215.29
      + 38.75

SRB
34–36

---

2. Complete the "What's My Rule?" table, and state the rule.

Rule

in	out
240	8
600	20
	12
	50
2,100	
1,200	

SRB
231 232

---

3. Find the least common denominator for the fraction pairs.

a. $\frac{2}{7}$ and $\frac{1}{3}$ _____

b. $\frac{5}{8}$ and $\frac{4}{16}$ _____

c. $\frac{3}{8}$ and $\frac{4}{12}$ _____

d. $\frac{2}{5}$ and $\frac{2}{3}$ _____

e. $\frac{4}{16}$ and $\frac{6}{12}$ _____

f. $\frac{5}{15}$ and $\frac{2}{8}$ _____

SRB
65

---

4. Elena received the following scores on math tests: 80, 85, 76, 70, 87, 80, 90, 80, and 90.

Find the following landmarks:

maximum: _____

minimum: _____

range: _____

mode: _____

mean: _____

SRB
119

---

5. Use the graph to answer the questions.

a. Which day had the greatest attendance? _____

b. What was the total attendance for the five-day period? _____

Movie Theater Attendance

Number of Tickets Sold

30
25
20
15
10
5
0

M Tu W Th F
Day of the Week

SRB
124

LESSON 9·9 Volume of Prisms

The volume *V* of any prism can be found with the formula $V = B * h$, where *B* is the area of the base of the prism, and *h* is the height of the prism from that base.

Find the volume of each prism.

1.

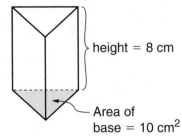

height = 8 cm

Area of base = 10 cm²

Volume = _____ cm³

2.

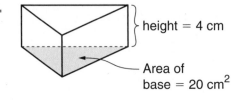

height = 4 cm

Area of base = 20 cm²

Volume = _____ cm³

3.

10 cm

6 cm

12 cm

Volume = _____ cm³

4.

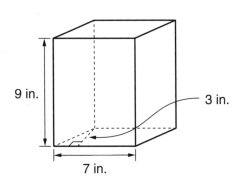

9 in.

3 in.

7 in.

Volume = _____ in³

5.

3 ft

Area of base = 15 ft²

Volume = _____ ft³

6.

6 cm

5.7 cm

4 cm

4 cm

Volume = _____ cm³

Measurement and Geometry 1.0, **1.3**, 1.4

LESSON 9·9

Volume of Prisms *continued*

7.

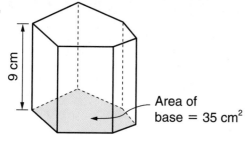

9 cm

Area of base = 35 cm²

Volume = _____ cm³

8.

8 cm

3 cm

6.5 cm

Volume = _____ cm³

9.

5.5 in.

3 in.

11 in.

Volume = _____ in³

10.

6 cm

5 cm

3 cm

5 cm

4 cm

Volume = _____ cm³

11.

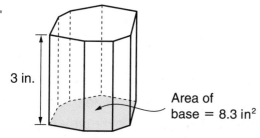

3 in.

Area of base = 8.3 in²

Volume = _____ in³

12.

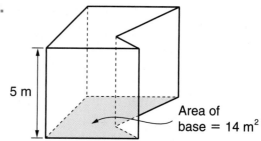

5 m

Area of base = 14 m²

Volume = _____ m³

LESSON 9·9   **Math Boxes**

---

1. a. Plot the following points on the grid:

$(-4,-1); (-3,1); (1,3); (2,1); (-2,-1)$

b. Connect the points with line segments in the order given above. Then connect $(-4,-1)$ and $(-2,-1)$.

What shape have you drawn?

_____

208

---

2. Find the diameter of the circle. Choose the best answer.

◯ 48 units

◯ 66 units

◯ 44 units

◯ 11 units

153

---

3. What transformation does the figure show? Circle the best answer.

A translation   preimage   image

B reflection

C rotation

D dilation

157 158

---

4. a. What is the perimeter of the rectangle?

_____

6 units

9 units

b. What is the area?

_____

186

---

5. Two cups of flour are needed to make 24 oatmeal cookies. How many cups of flour are needed to make...

a. 4 dozen cookies? _____ cups

b. 6 dozen cookies? _____ cups

c. 120 cookies? _____ cups

108 109

---

1) MR 2.3   2) MG **2.1**   3) MR **2.3**
4) MG 1.4   5) MR **1.1**

LESSON 9·10 Units of Volume and Capacity

In the metric system, units of length, volume, capacity, and weight are related.

◆ The **cubic centimeter (cm³)** is a metric unit of volume.

◆ The **liter (L)** and **milliliter (mL)** are units of capacity.

1. Complete.

   a. 1 liter (L) = _____ milliliters (mL).

   b. There are _____ cubic centimeters (cm³) in 1 liter.

   c. So 1 cm³ = _____ mL.

2. The cube in the diagram has sides 5 cm long.

   a. What is the volume of the cube?

      _____ cm³

   b. If the cube were filled with water, how many milliliters would it hold?

      _____ mL

3. **a.** What is the volume of the rectangular prism in the drawing?

      _____ cm³

   b. If the prism were filled with water, how many milliliters would it hold?

      _____ mL

   c. That is what fraction of a liter?

      _____ L

Complete.

4. 2 L = _____ mL   **5.** 350 cm³ = _____ mL   **6.** 1,500 mL = _____ L

LESSON 9·10

Units of Volume and Capacity *continued*

7. One liter of water weighs about 1 kilogram (kg).

50 cm

20 cm

40 cm

If the tank in the diagram above is filled with
water, about how much will the water weigh? About _____ kg

In the U.S. customary system, units of length and capacity are not closely related.
Larger units of capacity are multiples of smaller units.

◆ 1 cup (c) = 8 fluid ounces (fl oz)

◆ 1 pint (pt) = 2 cups (c)

◆ 1 quart (qt) = 2 pints (pt)

◆ 1 gallon (gal) = 4 quarts (qt)

8. a. 1 gallon = _____ quarts

   b. 1 gallon = _____ pints

9. a. 2 quarts = _____ pints

   b. 2 quarts = _____ fluid ounces

10. Sometimes it is helpful to know that 1 liter is a little more than 1 quart. In the
United States, gasoline is sold by the gallon. If you travel in other parts of the
world, you will find that gasoline is sold by the liter. Is 1 gallon of gasoline more or
less than 4 liters of gasoline?

_____

Measurement and Geometry **1.3**, 1.4

LESSON 9·10 Open Boxes

What are the dimensions of an open box—having the greatest possible volume—that can be made out of a single sheet of centimeter grid paper?

1. Use centimeter grid paper to experiment until you discover a pattern. Record your results in the table below.

Height of box	Length of base	Width of base	Volume of box
1 cm	20 cm	14 cm	
2 cm			
3 cm			

2. What are the dimensions of the box with the greatest volume?

Height of box = _____ cm   Length of base = _____ cm

Width of base = _____ cm   Volume of box = _____ cm³

More Practice with the Rectangle Method

Use the rectangle method to find the area of each triangle and parallelogram below.

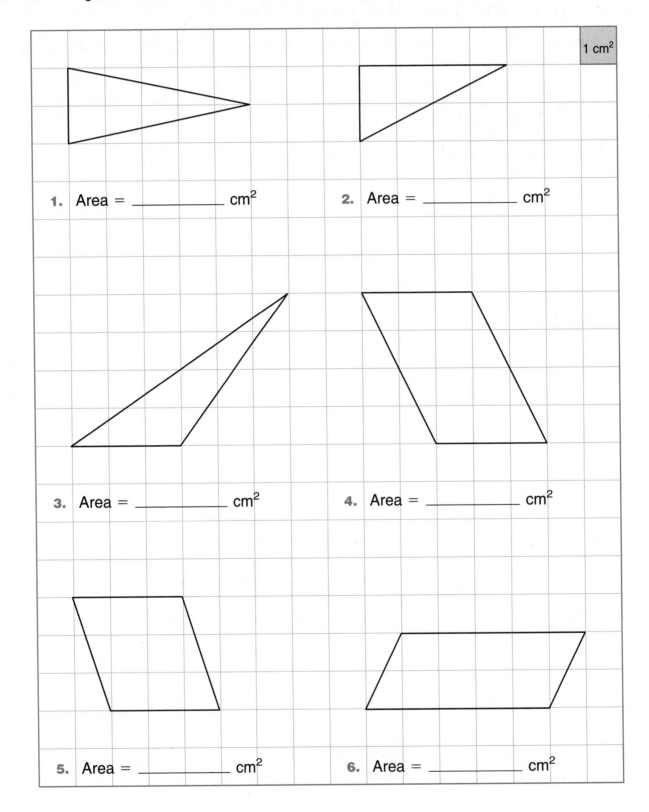

1 cm²

1. Area = _____ cm²

2. Area = _____ cm²

3. Area = _____ cm²

4. Area = _____ cm²

5. Area = _____ cm²

6. Area = _____ cm²

Measurement and Geometry 1.0; Measurement and Geometry **1.1**

LESSON 9·10 **Math Boxes**

---

1. Solve.

a.	40.017 + 269.000	**b.**	24.303 + 5.700
c.	402.03 − 24.70	**d.**	590.32 − 465.75

SRB 34–36

---

2. Complete the "What's My Rule?" table, and state the rule.

Rule	in	out
	40	
	80	10
		9
		8
	56	7

SRB 231 232

---

3. Monroe said that the least common denominator for $\frac{5}{20}$ and $\frac{2}{3}$ was 60.

Is he correct? _____

Rename the fractions using the least common denominator.

_____ and _____

SRB 65

---

4. The table below shows the student attendance for after school clubs at Lincoln Elementary School.

Mon	Tue	Wed	Thur	Fri
35	25	30	24	24

Find the following landmarks for this data.

minimum: _____   mode: _____

maximum: _____   median: _____

range: _____   mean: _____

SRB 119

---

5. Use the graph to answer the questions.

a. Which month had the most days of outside recess? _____

b. What was the total number of days of outside recess? _____

Days of Outside Recess

LESSON 9·11 **Math Boxes**

---

1. The prism to the right is made of centimeter cubes.

   What is the area of the base?

   _____

   What is the volume of the prism?

   _____

   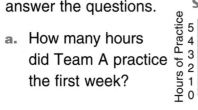
   SRB 189 197

2. A person breathes an average of 12 to 15 times per minute. At this rate, about how many breaths would a person take in a day?

   _____

   Explain how you got your answer.

   _____

   _____

   _____

   SRB 102 103

---

3. Use the graph to answer the questions.

   a. How many hours did Team A practice the first week?

      _____

   b. How many hours did they practice in the 5-week period?

      _____

   Team A Soccer Practice

   SRB 124

4. If the radius of a circle is 2.5 inches, what is its diameter?

   SRB 153

   _____

   Explain. _____

   _____

   _____

   _____

---

5. Explain how you could find the area of the rectangle below.

   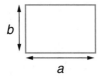

   _____

   _____

   SRB 189

6. Write an open number sentence for the story. Then solve.

   Kashawn swims 680 laps each week. How many laps does he swim in 5 weeks?

   Open number sentence:

   _____

   Solution: _____

   SRB 19 20 219

---

1) MG 1.3 2) MR 2.5 3) AF 1.1
4) MR 2.5 5) MG 1.4 6) MR 2.2

LESSON 10·1 Pan-Balance Problems

Math Message

1. Explain how to use a pan balance to weigh an object.

_____

_____

_____

_____

_____

Solve these pan-balance problems. In each figure, the two pans are in perfect balance.

2. One cube weighs as

   much as _____ marbles.

3. One cube weighs

   as much as _____ oranges.

4. One whole orange weighs

   as much as _____ grapes.

5. One block weighs

   as much as _____ marbles.

Check your answers. The sum of the answers to Problems 2–5 should equal $39\frac{1}{2}$.

LESSON 10·1 **Pan-Balance Problems** *continued*

6. One ☐ weighs
   as much as _____ △ s.

☐ ☐ △   ☐ △ △ △

7. One ☐ weighs
   as much as _____ marbles.

5 ☐ ⊘⊘⊘   ☐ ☐ ⊘⊘⊘⊘ ⊘⊘⊘⊘⊘

8. One *x* weighs
   as much as _____ balls.

3*x*   1 ball   *x*   7 balls

9. One *u* weighs
   as much as _____ *V*s.

4*u* + 3*V*   3*u* + 6*V*

Check your answers: The sum of the answers to Problems 6–9 should equal 10.

Try This

10. An empty bottle weighs as much as 6 marbles.

  a. The content within a full bottle weighs

     as much as _____ marbles.

  b. A full bottle weighs as much as _____ marbles.

  c. Explain your solutions.

_____

_____

_____

_____

_____

_____

_____

_____

_____

Algebra and Functions 1.0, 1.1; Mathematical Reasoning 2.3

Date _____ Time _____

---

1. Write the coordinates of the points shown on the coordinate grid.

   a. A: _____

   b. B: _____

   c. C: _____

   d. D: _____

208

---

2. Add or subtract.

   a. $-7 + (-3)$ = _____

   b. $5 - (-8)$ = _____

   c. $-17 + 10$ = _____

   d. $-15 - 15$ = _____

   e. $3 + (-20)$ = _____

   SRB 92

3. Multiply. Use an algorithm of your choice. Show your work.

   a.
   $$\begin{array}{r} 87 \\ * 65 \\ \hline \end{array}$$

   b.
   $$\begin{array}{r} 39 \\ * 24 \\ \hline \end{array}$$

   c.
   $$\begin{array}{r} 99 \\ * 26 \\ \hline \end{array}$$

   SRB 19

---

4. Find the radius and diameter of the circle.

   radius = _____
                    (unit)

   diameter = _____
                       (unit)

   SRB 153

5. The volume of this prism is 180 cubic units.

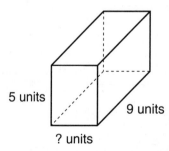

5 units   9 units

? units

   What is the width of its base?

   _____

   SRB 197

LESSON 10·2 More Pan-Balance Problems

Math Message

Solve these pan-balance problems. In each figure, the two pans are in perfect balance.

1. One block weighs

   as much as _____ balls.

2. One ball weighs

   as much as _____ marbles.

Solve these problems using both pan balances. In each problem, the pans are in perfect balance. The weights of objects, such as blocks, balls, marbles, and coins, are consistent within each problem.

3.

   One block weighs

   as much as _____ marbles.

   One coin weighs

   as much as _____ marbles.

4.
   One block weighs

   as much as _____ marbles.

   One ball weighs

   as much as _____ marbles.

5.

   One block weighs

   as much as _____ marbles.

   One ball weighs

   as much as _____ marbles.

Algebra and Functions 1.0, 1.1; Mathematical Reasoning 1.0, 2.3

LESSON 10·2 More Pan-Balance Problems continued

6.

One coin weighs

as much as _____ clips.

One block weighs

as much as _____ clips.

7.

One can weighs

as much as _____ blocks.

One doughnut weighs

as much as _____ blocks.

8.

One □ weighs

as much as _____ marbles.

One △ weighs

as much as _____ marbles.

9.

Each can weighs B ounces.

$B =$ _____ ounces

Each cube weighs A ounces.

$A =$ _____ ounces

LESSON 10·2   More Pan-Balance Problems *continued*

10.

One ☐ weighs

as much as ——— marbles.

One △ weighs

as much as ——— marbles.

11.

y weighs

as much as _____ marbles.

x weighs

as much as _____ marbles.

12.

If the cup is full, the coffee *in* the cup weighs as much as _____ marbles.

If the cup is full, the coffee *plus* the cup weighs as much as _____ marbles.

13. Two pens weigh as much as one compass. One pen and one compass together weigh 45 grams.

Complete the pan-balance problems below. Find the weights of one pen and one compass.

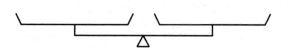

One pen weighs _____ grams.

One compass weighs _____ grams.

Algebra and Functions 1.0, 1.1; Mathematical Reasoning 1.0, 2.2, 2.3

LESSON 10·2 **Line Graphs**

1. Use the graph to answer the questions.

   a. Did the temperature increase or decrease between 1:00 P.M. and 2:00 P.M.?

   _____

   b. Did the temperature increase any time during the afternoon?

   _____

   c. How many degrees did the temperature change in 5 hours?

   _____

February Temperature Readings

   d. What do you think the temperature will be at 7:00 P.M.? _____

   Explain your answer.

   _____

   _____

   _____

2. Make a line graph for the following data set.

Puppy Weight Gain

   Write two true statements about the information on the graph.

   _____

   _____

   _____

LESSON 10·2 | **Math Boxes**

---

1. Make a magnitude estimate for the product. Choose the best answer.

4,246 * 2.5

⬭ tenths

⬭ ones

⬭ hundreds

⬭ thousands

⬭ ten-thousands

SRB 247—250

2. Circle the numbers below that are divisible by 6.

148   293   762   1,050   984

SRB 11

---

3. Name the number for each point marked on the number line.

A = _____   B = _____   C = _____

D = _____   E = _____   F = _____

SRB 57

---

4. a. Which has the greater area, a 3 ft × 2 ft rectangle or a triangle with base 3 ft and height 5 ft?

_____

b. Which has the greater area, a triangle with base 10 cm and height 4 cm or a parallelogram with base 5 cm and height 6 cm?

_____

SRB 189 192 193

5. Find the volume of the prism. Fill in the circle next to the best answer.

Volume = length * width * height

5 ft   15 ft   3 ft

○ **A.** 252 ft^3

○ **B.** 50 ft^3

○ **C.** 23 ft^3

○ **D.** 225 ft^3

SRB 197

---

1) MR 2.1   2) MR 2.0   3) NS 1.5
4) MG 1.4   5) MG 1.3

LESSON 10·3 Algebraic Expressions

Complete each statement below with an algebraic expression, using the suggested variable. The first problem has been done for you.

1. If Beth's allowance is $2.50 more than Kesia's, then Beth's allowance is

   _____ $D + \$2.50$ _____.

   Kesia's allowance   Beth
   is *D* dollars.

2. If Leon gets a raise of $5 per week, then his salary is

   _____.

   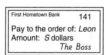

   Leon's salary is
   S dollars per week.

3. If Ali's grandfather is 50 years older than Ali, then Ali is

   _____ years old.

   Ali's grandfather   Ali
   is *G* years old.

4. Seven baskets of potatoes weigh

   _____ pounds.

   A basket of potatoes
   weighs *P* pounds.

LESSON 10·3   **Algebraic Expressions** *continued*

5. If a submarine dives 150 feet,
   then it will be traveling at a depth of

   _____ feet.

A submarine is traveling
at a depth of *X* feet.

6. The floor is divided into 5 equal-size
   areas for gym classes. Each class
   has a playing area of

   _____ ft².

The gym floor has an
area of *A* square feet.

7. The charge for a book that is
   D days overdue is

   _____ cents.

Sports
Heroes

A library charges 10 cents for each
overdue book. It adds an additional
charge of 5 cents per day for each
overdue book.

8. If Kevin spends $\frac{2}{3}$ of his allowance on
   a book, then he has

   _____ dollars left.

Kevin's allowance
is *X* dollars.

Algebra and Functions **1.2**

LESSON 10·3 **"What's My Rule?"**

1. **a.** State in words the rule for the "What's My Rule?" table at the right.

   _____

   _____

   _____

   _____

X	Y
5	1
4	0
−1	−5
1	−3
2	−2

   b. Circle the number sentence that describes the rule.

   $Y = X / 5$ $\qquad$ $Y = X − 4$ $\qquad$ $Y = 4 − X$

2. **a.** State in words the rule for the "What's My Rule?" table at the right.

   _____

   _____

   _____

   _____

Q	Z
1	3
3	5
−4	−2
−3	−1
−2.5	−0.5

   b. Circle the number sentence that describes the rule.

   $Z = Q + 2$ $\qquad$ $Z = 2 * Q$ $\qquad$ $Z = \frac{1}{2}Q * 1$

3. **a.** State in words the rule for the "What's My Rule?" table at the right.

   _____

   _____

   _____

   _____

g	t
$\frac{1}{2}$	2
0	0
2.5	10
$\frac{1}{4}$	1
5	20

   b. Circle the number sentence that describes the rule.

   $g = 2 * t$ $\qquad$ $t = 2 * g$ $\qquad$ $t = 4 * g$

Math Boxes

1. Identify the point named by each ordered number pair.

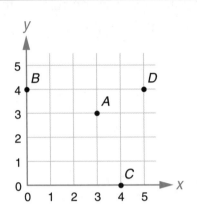

a. (0,4) _____

b. (3,3) _____

c. (5,4) _____

d. (4,0) _____

SRB 208

2. Add or subtract.

a. $20 + (-10) =$ _____

b. $-8 + (-17) =$ _____

c. $-12 - (-12) =$ _____

d. $-45 + 45 =$ _____

e. $-31 - 14 =$ _____

SRB 92

3. Multiply. Use an algorithm of your choice. Show your work.

a.   43
   * 78

b.   19
   * 86

c.   79
   * 42

SRB 19

4. a. Draw a circle that has a diameter of 4 centimeters.

SRB 153 164

b. The radius of the circle is _____.

5. The rectangular prism below has a volume of 126 cubic centimeters.

Area of base = 42 cm²

What is the height of the prism? _____
(unit)

SRB 197

1) SDAP 1.4   2) NS 2.1   3) MR 2.0
4) MG 1.4   5) MG 1.3

LESSON 10·4 **Math Boxes**

---

1. Make a magnitude estimate for the product. Choose the best answer.

0.4 * 6.5

⬭ tenths

⬭ ones

⬭ hundreds

⬭ thousands

⬭ ten-thousands

SRB
247–250

2. Circle the numbers below that are divisible by 9.

3,735   2,043   192   769   594

SRB
11

---

3. a. Mark and label −1.7, 0.8, −1.3, and 1.9 on the number line.

-2   -1   0   1   2

b. What number is 1 less than −1.7? _____

c. What number is 1 more than 1.9? _____

SRB
92–94

---

4. Circle the figure below that has the same area as Figure A.

A

SRB
189

5. Find the volume of the prism. Circle the best answer.

Volume = length * width * height

3 ft
5 ft
2 ft

A   10 ft³

B   30 ft³

C   17 ft³

D   60 ft³

SRB
197

LESSON 10·4   Speed and Distance

Math Message

1. A plane travels at a speed of 480 miles per hour. At that rate, how many miles will it travel in 1 minute? Write a number model to show what you did to solve the problem.

   Number model: _____   Distance per minute: _____ miles

Rule for Distance Traveled

2. For an airplane flying at 8 miles per minute (480 mph), you can use the following rule to calculate the distance traveled for any number of minutes:

> Distance traveled = 8 * number of minutes
> or
> $d = 8 * t$

   where d stands for the distance traveled in miles and t for the time of travel in minutes. For example, after 1 minute, the plane will have traveled 8 miles (8 * 1). After 2 minutes, it will have traveled 16 miles (8 * 2).

3. Use the rule $d = 8 * t$ to complete the table at the right.

Time (min) (t)	Distance (mi) ($8 * t$)
1	8
2	16
3	
4	
5	
6	
7	
8	
9	
10	

Algebra and Functions 1.0, 1.1, **1.2**, **1.5**; Statistics, Data Analysis, and Probability 1.1, **1.4**

LESSON 10·4 Speed and Distance *continued*

4. Complete the graph using the data in the table on page 346. Then connect the dots.

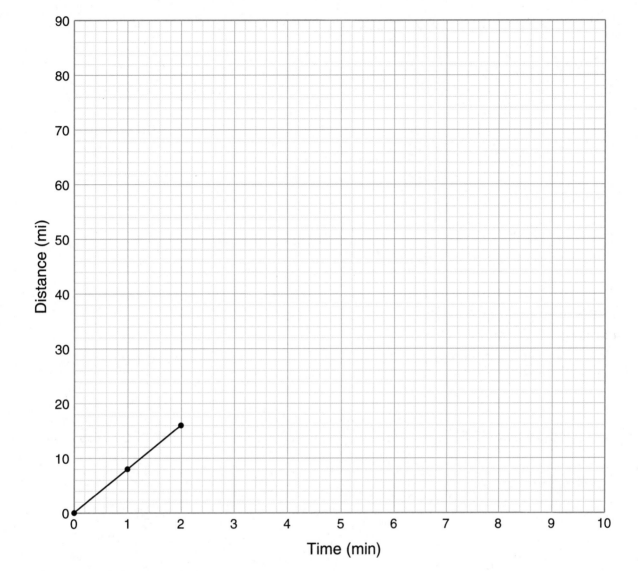

Use your graph to answer the following questions.

5. How far would the plane travel in $1\frac{1}{2}$ minutes?   _____
(unit)

6. How many miles would the plane travel in
5 minutes 24 seconds (5.4 minutes)?   _____
(unit)

7. How long would it take the plane to travel 60 miles?   _____
(unit)

LESSON 10·4 Representing Rates

Complete each table below. Then graph the data and connect the points.

1. **a.** Andy earns $8 per hour.   Rule: Earnings = $8 * number of hours worked

Time (hr) (h)	Earnings ($) (8 * h)
1	
2	
3	
	40
7	

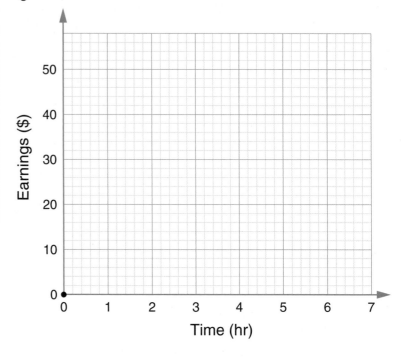

b. Plot a point to show Andy's earnings for $5\frac{1}{2}$ hours. How much would he earn?

_____

2. **a.** Red peppers cost $2.50 per pound.   Rule: Cost = $2.50 * number of pounds

Weight (lb) (w)	Cost ($) (2.50 * w)
1	
2	
3	
	15.00
12	

b. Plot a point to show the cost of 8 pounds. How much would 8 pounds of red peppers cost?

_____

Algebra and Functions 1.0, **1.2**, **1.5**; Statistics, Data Analysis, and Probability 1.1, **1.4**

**LESSON
10·4**   **Representing Rates** *continued*

3. **a.** Frank types an average of 45 words per minute.

Rule: Words typed = 45 * number of minutes

Time (min) (t)	Words (45 * t)
1	
2	
3	
	225
6	

b. Plot a point to show the number of words Frank types in 4 minutes. How many words is that?

_____

4. **a.** Joan's car uses 1 gallon of gasoline every 28 miles.

Rule: Distance = 28 * number of gallons

Gasoline (gal) (g)	Distance (mi) (28 * g)
1	
2	
3	
	140
$5\frac{1}{2}$	

b. Plot a point to show how far the car would travel on 1.4 gallons of gasoline. How many miles would it go?

_____

LESSON 10·5 Predicting When Old Faithful Will Erupt

Old Faithful Geyser in Yellowstone National Park is one of nature's most impressive sights. Yellowstone has 200 geysers and thousands of hot springs, mud pots, steam vents, and other "hot spots"—more than any other place on Earth. Old Faithful is not the largest or tallest geyser in Yellowstone, but it is the most dependable. Using the length of time for an eruption, park rangers can predict when further eruptions will occur.

Old Faithful erupts at regular intervals that are **predictable.** If you time the length of one eruption, you can **predict** about how long you must wait until the next eruption. Use this formula:

Waiting time = (10 * (length of eruption)) + 30 minutes

$$W = (10 * E) + 30$$
$$W = 10E + 30$$

> All times are in minutes.

1. Use the formula to complete the table below.

Length of Eruption (min) (E)	Waiting Time to Next Eruption (min) ((10 * E) + 30)
2 min	50 min
3 min	_____ min
4 min	_____ min
5 min	_____ min
1 min	_____ min
$2\frac{1}{2}$ min	_____ min
3 min 15 sec	_____ min
_____ min	45 min

2. Graph the data from the table. One number pair has been plotted for you.

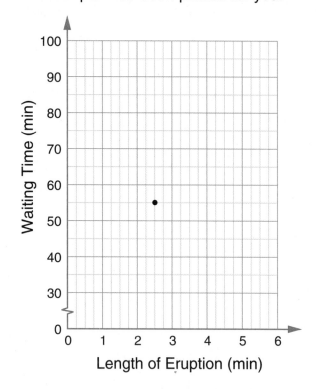

3. It's 8:30 A.M., and Old Faithful has just finished a 4-minute eruption. About when will it erupt next?

_____

4. The average time between eruptions of Old Faithful is about 75 minutes. So the average length of an eruption is about how many minutes?

_____

Algebra and Functions 1.0, 1.1, **1.2**, **1.5**; Statistics, Data Analysis, and Probability **1.4**; Mathematical Reasoning 2.3, 3.0

Date _____ Time _____

More Pan-Balance Practice

Solve these pan-balance problems. In each figure, the two pans are in perfect balance.

1.

One orange weighs

as much as _____ triangle.

2.

One marble weighs

as much as _____ pencil.

3.

One doughnut weighs

as much as _____ X s.

4.

One S weighs

as much as _____ P.

5.

One triangle weighs as much as _____ paper clips.

Explain how you found your answer. _____

_____

_____

_____

_____

_____

6.

One X weighs as much as _____ M.

LESSON 10·5 Math Boxes

---

1. Write an expression to answer the question.

a. Maria is *y* years old. Sheila is 10 years older than Maria. How old is Sheila?

_____ years old

b. Franklin has *c* miniature cards. Rosie has 4 more cards than twice the number Franklin has. How many cards does Rosie have?

_____ cards

c. Lucinda goes to camp for *d* days each summer. Rhonda goes to camp 1 day less than half of Lucinda's number of days. For how many days does Rhonda go to camp?

_____ days

d. Cheryl read *b* books this year. Ralph read 3 more than 5 times as many books as Cheryl. How many books did Ralph read?

_____ books

 SRB 218

---

2. Use a calculator to rename each of the following in standard notation.

a. $7^3 =$ _____

b. $9^5 =$ _____

c. $4^5 =$ _____

d. $6^8 =$ _____

e. $3^7 =$ _____

SRB 6

3. Solve.   Solution

a. $6 = 20 + s$ _____

b. $18 + t = -2$ _____

c. $-15 + u = -23$ _____

d. $-11 - v = -5$ _____

e. $29 - w = 35$ _____

SRB 92–94 219

---

4. Complete the "What's My Rule?" table and state the rule.

Rule: _____

in	out
8	
	−2
2	−6
0	
	9

SRB 231 232

5. Find the area.

Area of a Triangle
$A = \frac{1}{2} * b * h$

7 units

4 units

Area: _____

SRB 193

---

1) AF 1.2   2) NS 1.3   3) AF 1.2
4) MR 1.1   5) MG 1.1

LESSON 10·6 Math Boxes

1. Below are the distances (in feet) that a baseball must travel to right field to be a home run in various major league baseball parks.

330	353	330	345	325	330	325	338	318
302	333	347	325	315	330	327	314	348

a. Make a stem-and-leaf plot for the data.

Identify the landmarks.

Stems (100s and 10s)	Leaves (1s)

b. What is the maximum? _____

c. What is the mode? _____

d. What is the median? _____

2. Solve.

a. 3.26 + 504.1 = _____

b. _____ = 793.82 − 209.785

c. _____ = 987.55 + 283.6

d. 24.07 − 6.434 = _____

e. _____ = 9.775 + 0.03

f. 21.574 + 179.48 = _____

3. Complete the following equivalents.

a. 1 pint = _____ cups

b. 1 quart = _____ pints

c. 1 quart = _____ cups

d. 1 gallon = _____ quarts

e. 1 gallon = _____ cups

LESSON 10·6 Rules, Tables, and Graphs

Math Message

1. Use the graph below. Find the *x*- and *y*-coordinates of each point shown. Then enter the *x* and *y* values in the table.

x	y
2	3

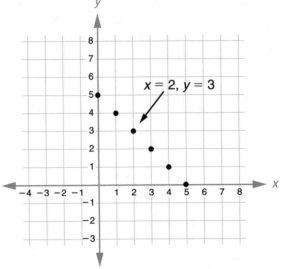

x = 2, *y* = 3

---

2. Eli is 10 years old and can run an average of 5 yards per second. His sister Lupita is 7 and can run an average of 4 yards per second.

   Eli and Lupita have a 60-yard race. Because Lupita is younger, Eli gives her a 10-yard head start.

   Complete the table showing the distances Eli and Lupita are from the starting line after 1 second, 2 seconds, 3 seconds, and so on. Use the table to answer the questions below.

   a. Who wins the race? _____

   b. What is the winning time?

   _____

   c. Who was in the lead during most of the race? _____

Time (sec)	Distance (yd)	
	Eli	**Lupita**
start	0	10
1		
2		18
3	15	
4		
5		
6		
7		38
8		
9		
10		
11		
12		

Algebra and Functions 1.0, 1.1, **1.2**, **1.5**; Statistics, Data Analysis, and Probability **1.4**, 1.5; Mathematical Reasoning 2.3

LESSON 10·6

Rules, Tables, and Graphs *continued*

3. Use the grid below to graph the results of the race between Eli and Lupita.

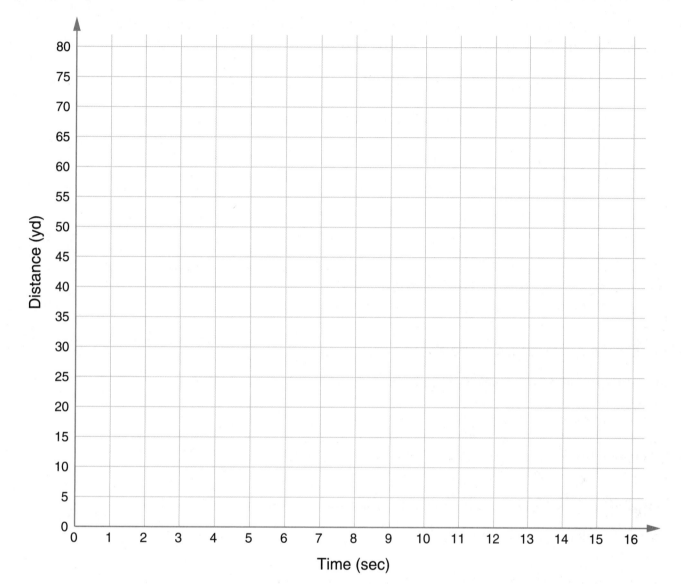

Distance (yd)

Time (sec)

4. How many yards apart are Eli and Lupita after 7 seconds?   _____

5. Suppose Eli and Lupita race for 75 yards instead
of 60 yards.

   a. Who would you expect to win?   _____

   b. How long would the race last?   _____ seconds

   c. How far ahead would the winner be at the finish line?   _____ yards

LESSON 10·7   Running-and-Walking Graph

Math Message

Tamara, William, and Imani timed themselves traveling the same distance in different ways. Tamara ran, William walked, and Imani walked toe-to-heel.

After they timed themselves, they drew a graph.

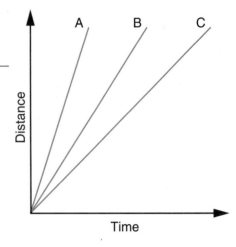

1. Which line on the graph at the right is for Tamara? _____

2. Which line is for William? _____

3. Which line is for Imani? _____

4. JaDerrick came along later and was the slowest of all. He walked heel-to-toe backward. Draw a line on the graph to show the speed you think JaDerrick walked.

Review: Algebraic Expressions

Complete each statement with an algebraic expression.

5. Alberto is 5 years older than Rick. If Rick is R years old,

   then Alberto is _____ years old.

6. Rebecca's piano lesson is half as long as Kendra's. If Kendra's piano lesson is

   K minutes long, then Rebecca's is _____ minutes long.

7. Marlin's dog weighs 3 pounds more than twice the weight of Eddy's dog.

   If Eddy's dog weighs E pounds, then Marlin's dog weighs _____ pounds.

Algebra and Functions 1.1, 1.2; Statistics, Data Analysis, and Probability 1.2, 1.4

LESSON 10·7 **Reading Graphs**

1. Tom and Alisha run a 200-yard race. Tom has a head start.

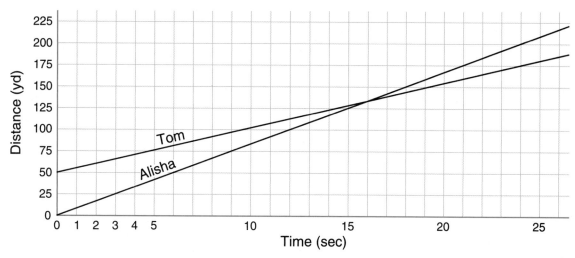

a. Who wins the race? _____

b. By about how much? _____

c. Mark the point on the graph where Alisha overtakes Tom.

d. About how many yards does Alisha run before taking the lead? _____

e. About how many seconds pass before Alisha takes the lead? _____

f. Who is ahead after 9 seconds? _____

g. By about how much? _____

2. Ahmed is definitely out of shape, but he runs 100 meters as fast as he can.

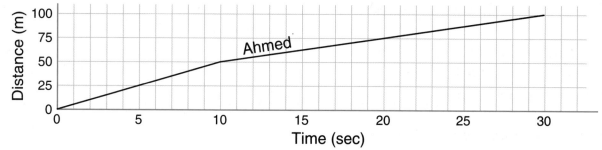

a. In the first 10 seconds of his run, Ahmed covers about _____ meters,

and his speed is about $\dfrac{\boxed{}\ \text{meters}}{10\ \text{seconds}} = \dfrac{\boxed{}\ \text{meters}}{1\ \text{second}}$.

b. In the final 10 seconds of his run, Ahmed covers about _____ meters,

and his speed is about $\dfrac{\boxed{}\ \text{meters}}{10\ \text{seconds}} = \dfrac{\boxed{}\ \text{meters}}{1\ \text{second}}$.

Algebra and Functions 1.1; Statistics, Data Analysis, and Probability 1.2, **1.4**

LESSON 10·7 Mystery Graphs

Each of the events described below is represented by one of the following graphs.

Graph A   Graph B   Graph C   Graph D   Graph E

Match each event with its graph.

1. A frozen dinner is removed from the freezer. It is heated in a microwave oven. Then it is placed on the table.

   Which graph shows the temperature of the dinner at different times?   Graph _____

2. Satya runs water into his bathtub. He steps into the tub, sits down, and bathes. He gets out of the tub and drains the water.

   Which graph shows the height of water in the tub at different times?   Graph _____

3. A baseball is thrown straight up into the air.

   a. Which graph shows the height of the ball—from the time it is thrown until the time it hits the ground?   Graph _____

   b. Which graph shows the speed of the ball at different times?   Graph _____

Algebra and Functions 1.1; Statistics, Data Analysis, and Probability 1.2, **1.4**

LESSON 10·7

Math Boxes

1. Shenequa is y years old. Write an algebraic expression for the age of each person below.

   a. Nancy is 4 years older than Shenequa. Nancy's age: _____ years

   b. Francisco is twice as old as Shenequa. Francisco's age: _____ years

   c. Jose is $\frac{1}{3}$ as old as Shenequa. Jose's age: _____ years

   d. Lucienne is 8 years younger than Shenequa. Lucienne's age: _____ years

   e. If Shenequa is 12 years old, who is the oldest person listed above? _____

   How old is that person? _____

   SRB 218

---

2. Use a calculator to rename each of the following in standard notation.

   a. $3^{12} =$ _____

   b. $8^7 =$ _____

   c. $6^9 =$ _____

   d. $7^8 =$ _____

   e. $4^{11} =$ _____

    SRB 6

3. Solve.   Solution

   a. $\frac{3}{8} = \frac{a}{40}$ _____

   b. $-80 + c = 100$ _____

   c. $m * 25 = 400$ _____

   d. $s - 110 = -20$ _____

   e. $\frac{144}{z} = 12$ _____

    SRB 92–94 219

---

4. Complete the "What's My Rule?" table and state the rule.

   Rule: _____

in	out
$\frac{1}{3}$	
	0
$\frac{5}{3}$	4
	2
-2	$\frac{1}{3}$

    SRB 231 232

5. Find the area.

Area of Rectangles and Parallelograms
$A = b * h$

   Area: _____
   (unit)

    SRB 189 192

LESSON 10·8 A Problem from the National Assessment

The following problem was in the mathematics section of a 1975 national standardized test.

A square has a perimeter of 12 inches.
What is the area of the square?

1. Your answer: _____ in².

The table below gives the national results for this problem.

Answers	13-Year-Olds	17-Year-Olds	Young Adults
Correct answer	7%	28%	27%
144 sq inches	12%	19%	25%
48 sq inches	20%	10%	10%
24 sq inches	6%	4%	2%
12 sq inches	4%	3%	3%
6 sq inches	4%	2%	1%
3 sq inches	3%	2%	2%
Other incorrect answers	16%	13%	10%
No answer or "I don't know"	28%	19%	20%

Explain why many students might have given the following answers.

2. 144 square inches _____

_____

_____

3. 48 square inches _____

_____

_____

Measurement and Geometry 1.0; Measurement and Geometry 1.4; Mathematical Reasoning 2.4

LESSON 10·8 Ratio of Circumference to Diameter

You are going to explore the relationship between the circumference
and the diameter of a circle.

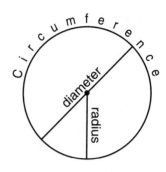

1. Using a metric tape measure, carefully measure the
   circumference and diameter of a variety of round
   objects. Measure to the nearest millimeter (one-tenth
   of a centimeter).

2. Record your data in the first three columns of the table below.

3. In the fourth column, write the ratio of the circumference to
   the diameter as a fraction.

4. In the fifth column, write the ratio as a decimal. Use your calculator
   to compute the decimal, and round your answer to two decimal places.

Object	Circumference (C)	Diameter (d)	Ratio of Circumference to Diameter	
			as a Fraction $\left(\dfrac{C}{d}\right)$	as a Decimal (from calculator)
Coffee cup	252 mm	80 mm	$\dfrac{252}{80}$	3.15
	_____ mm	_____ mm		
	_____ mm	_____ mm		
	_____ mm	_____ mm		
	_____ mm	_____ mm		
	_____ mm	_____ mm		

5. What is the median of the circumference-to-diameter ratios in the last column?

   _____

6. The students in your class combined their results in a stem-and-leaf plot. Use that
   plot to find the class median value for the ratio $\dfrac{C}{d}$.

   _____

LESSON 10·8 Converting Celsius to Fahrenheit

In the U.S. customary system, temperature is measured in degrees Fahrenheit (°F). The metric system measures temperature in degrees Celsius (°C). Water freezes at 0°C, or 32°F.

1. What temperature is shown on the thermometer at the right?

   _____

The following formula converts temperatures from degrees Celsius to degrees Fahrenheit, where F stands for the number of degrees Fahrenheit and C stands for the number of degrees Celsius:

Formula: $F = (1.8 * C) + 32$

A rule of thumb gives a rough estimate of the conversion.

Rule of thumb: Double the number of degrees Celsius and add the Fahrenheit freezing temperature.

$F = (2 * C) + 32$

2. Convert Celsius temperatures to Fahrenheit using the formula and the rule of thumb. Compare the results.

°C	−20	−10	0	10	20	30
°F (formula)						
°F (rule of thumb)						

3. Are the results from using the rule of thumb accurate in most situations? Explain.

   _____

   _____

4. Name one situation where you would use the formula rather than the rule of thumb to convert to degrees Fahrenheit. Explain.

   _____

   _____

5. Normal body temperature is 37°C or _____ F.

6. Water boils at 100°C or _____ F.

Number Sense 2.4; Algebra and Functions 1.5

LESSON 10·8 · Math Boxes

---

1. Below are the bowling scores from the Pick's family reunion bowling party.

106	135	168	130	116	109	139	162	161
130	118	105	150	164	130	138	112	116

a. Make a stem-and-leaf plot for the data.

Identify the landmarks.

b. What is the maximum score? _____

c. What is the mode for the scores? _____

d. What is the median score? _____

Stems (100s and 10s)	Leaves (1s)

118 119

---

2. Solve.

a. 52.6
    − 19.08

b. 703.93
    − 251.09

c. 826.3
    + 572.91

d. 262.75
    + 98.8

e. 78.92
    − 45.93

f. 486.387
    − 384.552

34–36

3. Complete the following equivalents.

a. 1 cup = _____ ounces

b. 1 pint = _____ ounces

c. 1 quart = _____ ounces

d. 4 quarts = _____ ounces

e. 1 gallon = _____ ounces

397

LESSON 10·9 Measuring the Area of a Circle

Math Message

Use the circle at the right to solve Problems 1−4.

1. The diameter of the circle is

   about _____ centimeters.

2. The radius of the circle is

   about _____ centimeters.

3. a. Write the open number sentence you would
   use to find the circumference of the circle.

   _____

   b. The circumference of the circle is

   about _____ centimeters.

4. Find the area of this circle by counting squares.

   About _____ cm²

---

5. What is the median of all the
   area measurements in your class? _____ cm²

6. Pi is the ratio of the circumference to the diameter of a circle. It is also
   the ratio of the area of a circle to the square of its radius. Write the
   formulas to find the circumference and the diameter of a circle that use
   these ratios.

   The formula for the circumference of a circle is _____ .

   The formula for the area of a circle is _____ .

Measurement and Geometry 1.0; Measurement and Geometry 1.4; Statistics, Data Analysis, and Probability 1.1

LESSON 10·9   Areas of Circles

Work with a partner. Use the same objects, but make separate measurements so you can check each other's work.

1. Trace several round objects onto the grid on *Math Masters*, page 436.

2. Count square centimeters to find the area of each circle.

3. Use a ruler to find the radius of each object. (*Reminder:* The radius is half the diameter.) Record your data in the first three columns of the table below.

Object	Area (sq cm)	Radius (cm)	Ratio of Area to Radius Squared	
			as a Fraction $\left(\frac{A}{r^2}\right)$	as a Decimal

4. Find the ratio of the area to the square of the radius for each circle. Write the ratio as a fraction in the fourth column of the table. Then use a calculator to compute the ratio as a decimal. Round your answer to two decimal places, and write it in the last column.

5. Find the median of the ratios in the last column. _____

LESSON 10·9   A Formula for the Area of a Circle

Your class just measured the area and the radius of many circles and found that the ratio of the area to the square of the radius is about 3.

This was no coincidence. Mathematicians proved long ago that the ratio of the area of a circle to the square of its radius is always equal to π. This can be written as:

$$\frac{A}{r^2} = \pi$$

Usually this fact is written in a slightly different form, as a formula for the area of a circle.

> The formula for the area of a circle is
> $$A = \pi * r^2$$
> where A is the area of a circle and r is its radius.

1. What is the radius of the circle in the Math Message on journal page 364? _____

2. Use the formula above to calculate the area of that circle. _____

3. Is the area you found by counting square centimeters
   more or less than the area you found by using the formula? _____

   How much more or less? _____

4. Use the formula to find the areas of the circles you traced on *Math Masters,* page 436.

   _____   _____   _____

5. Which do you think is a more accurate way to find the area of a circle, by counting squares or by measuring the radius and using the formula? Explain.

   _____

   _____

   _____

   _____

Measurement and Geometry 1.0; Mathematical Reasoning 2.4

LESSON 10·9 **Math Boxes**

---

1. Monica is *y* inches tall. Write an algebraic expression for the height of each person below.

   a. Tyrone is 8 inches taller than Monica. Tyrone's height: _____

   b. Isabel is $1\frac{1}{2}$ times as tall as Monica. Isabel's height: _____

   c. Chaska is 3 inches shorter than Monica. Chaska's height: _____

   d. Josh is $10\frac{1}{2}$ inches taller than Monica. Josh's height: _____

   e. If Monica is 48 inches tall, who is the tallest person listed above? _____

      How tall is that person? _____

   218

---

2. Use a calculator to rename each of the following in standard notation.

   a. $2^{17} =$ _____

   b. $7^6 =$ _____

   c. $6^{10} =$ _____

   d. $3^{10} =$ _____

   e. $5^9 =$ _____

   6

3. Solve.   Solution

   a. $-12 + d = 14$ _____

   b. $28 - e = -2$ _____

   c. $b + 18 = -24$ _____

   d. $-14 = f - 7$ _____

   e. $12 = 16 + g$ _____

   92–94
   219

---

4. Complete the "What's My Rule?" table and state the rule.

   Rule: _____

in	out
2	−10
	0
16	4
3	
	−5

   231 232

5. Find the volume of the cube.

   $$\boxed{\text{Volume} = \text{length} * \text{width} * \text{height}}$$

   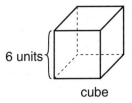

   6 units — cube

   Volume = _____

   196 197

LESSON 10·10   **Math Boxes**

---

1. Circle the rectangular prism below that has the greatest volume.

  4 cm 8 cm 7 cm

  7 cm 2 cm 12 cm

  4 cm 6 cm 9 cm

SRB
197

---

2. Write true or false for each statement.

a. A flat surface of a solid is called a face. _____

b. A rectangular prism has 6 faces. _____

c. Pyramids and cones have curved surfaces. _____

d. A rectangular pyramid has 5 faces. _____

SRB
147 148

3. Complete the following equivalents.

a. 1 cubic centimeter = _____ milliliter

b. 1 liter = _____ milliliters

c. 1 liter = _____ cubic centimeters

d. 1 kiloliter = _____ liters

e. 1 kiloliter = _____ milliliters

SRB
397

---

4. Find the area of each figure.

> Area of a triangle: $A = \frac{1}{2} * b * h$
> Area of a parallelogram: $A = b * h$

  9 in. 4 in.

  16 cm 9 cm

  15 yd 8 yd

Area: _____

Area: _____

Area: _____

SRB
192 193

---

1) MG 1.3   2) MG 2.0   3) MR 2.3
4) MG 1.1

LESSON 11·1   Geometric Solids

Each member of your group should cut out one of the patterns from *Math Masters,*
pages 323–326. Fold the pattern, and glue or tape it together. Then add this model to
your group's collection of geometric solids.

1. Examine your models of geometric solids.

   a. Which solids have all flat surfaces? _____

   _____

   b. Which have no flat surfaces? _____

   c. Which have both flat and curved surfaces? _____

   d. If you cut the label of a cylindrical can in a straight
   line perpendicular to the bottom and then unroll and
   flatten the label, what is the shape of the label?

   _____

   cut
   line

2. Examine your models of polyhedrons.

   a. Which polyhedrons have more faces than vertices? _____

   b. Which polyhedrons have the same number of faces and vertices? _____

   _____

   c. Which polyhedrons have fewer faces than vertices? _____

   _____

3. Examine your model of a cube.

   a. Does the cube have more edges than vertices, the same
   number of edges as vertices, or fewer edges than vertices? _____

   Is this true for all polyhedrons? _____ Explain. _____

   _____

   b. How many edges of the cube meet at each vertex? _____

   Is this true for all polyhedrons? _____ Explain. _____

   _____

Measurement and Geometry 2.0, 2.3

LESSON 11·1 Polyhedral Dice and Regular Polyhedrons

A set of polyhedral dice includes the following polyhedrons:

| Tetrahedral die | Octahedral die | Decahedral die | Dodecahedral die | Icosahedral die |

Examine the set of polyhedral dice that you have. Answer the following questions.

1. Which of the dice is not a **regular polyhedron?** Why? _____

   _____

2. Which regular polyhedron is missing from the set of polyhedral dice? _____

3. a. How many faces does an octahedron have?   _____ faces

   b. What shape are the faces?   _____

4. a. How many faces does a dodecahedron have?   _____ faces

   b. What shape are the faces?   _____

5. a. How many faces does an icosahedron have?   _____ faces

   b. What shape are the faces?   _____

6. Explain how the names of polyhedrons help you to know the number of their faces.

   _____

   _____

   _____

   _____

Measurement and Geometry 2.0, 2.3

LESSON 11·1 **Math Boxes**

---

1. Subtract.

   a. $10 - (-2) =$ _____

   b. $5 - 8 =$ _____

   c. $15 - (-5) =$ _____

   d. $-15 - (-5) =$ _____

   e. $-4 - 7 =$ _____

   SRB
   92–94

---

2. Which triangle is not congruent to the other three triangles? Circle the best answer.

   A.   **B.**

   C.   **D.**

   SRB
   155

---

3. The students in Ms. Divan's class took a survey of their favorite colors. Complete the table. Then make a circle graph of the data.

Favorite Color	Number of Students	Percent of Class
Red	6	
Blue	10	
Orange	4	
Yellow	2	
Purple	3	
Total		

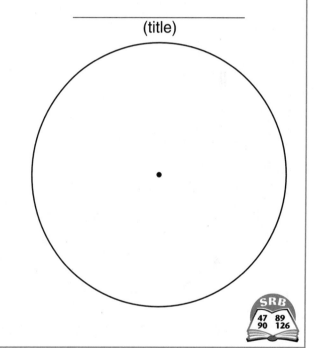

_____
(title)

SRB
47 89
90 126

---

4. Solve.

   a. $\frac{4}{5}$ of 25 = _____

   b. $\frac{5}{7}$ of 35 = _____

   c. $\frac{3}{12}$ of 16 = _____

   d. $\frac{6}{8}$ of 20 = _____

   e. $\frac{1}{2}$ of $\frac{1}{4}$ = _____

   SRB
   73

---

5. Write the prime factorization for 180.

   _____

   SRB
   12

LESSON 11·2 Comparing Geometric Solids

Math Message

Read *Student Reference Book,* pages 150 and 151 with a partner. Then make a Venn diagram to compare prisms and pyramids.

Prisms

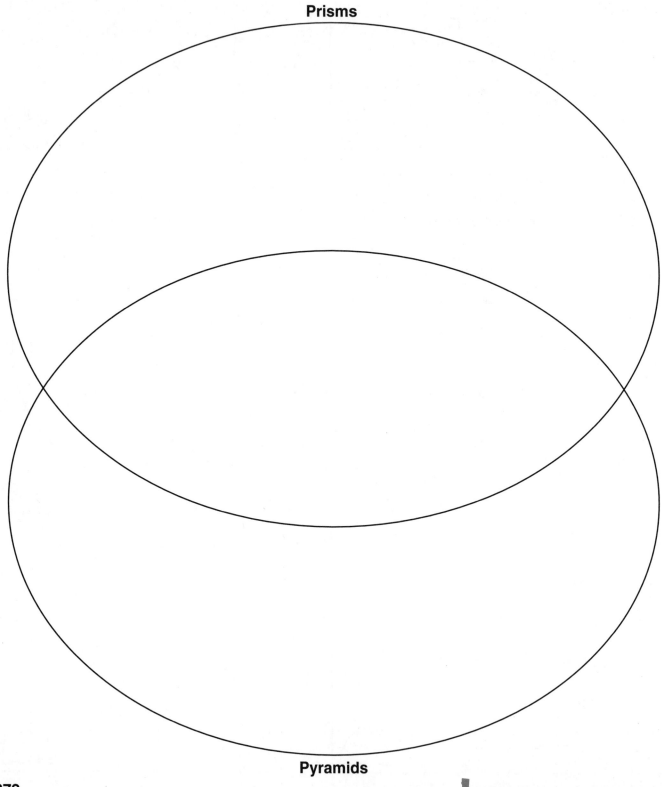

Pyramids

Measurement and Geometry 2.0, 2.3

Comparing Geometric Solids *continued*

List how the following geometric solids are alike and different.

	Prisms and Cylinders	Pyramids and Cones
Shapes		
Likenesses		
Differences		

LESSON 11·2 **Math Boxes**

---

1. Solve.

a. $\frac{1}{3}$ of 27 = _____

b. $\frac{1}{8}$ of 40 = _____

c. $\frac{1}{5}$ of 100 = _____

d. $\frac{2}{5}$ of 100 = _____

e. $\frac{1}{4}$ of 60 = _____

SRB 73

---

2. Find the volume of the prism.

5 units
8 units
5 units

Volume = $B * h$ where B is the area of the base and h is the height.

Volume: _____

SRB 197

---

3. To celebrate her birthday, Ms. Chang gives each of the fifth graders 1 piece of licorice. There are 179 fifth graders. The licorice comes in packages of 15 pieces, at a cost of $1.19 per package.

a. How many packages of licorice does Ms. Chang need to buy?

_____ packages

b. How much does she spend?

_____

SRB 22–24 243

---

4. Solve.

a. 2 gal = _____ qt

b. _____ pt = 2 qt

c. 8 c = _____ pt

d. 3 c = _____ fl oz

e. 1 qt = _____ fl oz

SRB 397

---

5. Make a factor tree to find the prime factorization of 100.

SRB 12

---

6. Kayin buys 6 envelopes for 14 cents each and 6 stamps for 39 cents each.

Which expression correctly represents how much money she spends? Circle the best answer.

A. $(6 + 6) * (14 + 39)$

B. $(6 * 6) + (14 * 39)$

C. $6 * (14 + 39)$

SRB 219

---

1) NS 2.5   2) MG 1.3   3) MR 1.1
4) MR 2.3   5) NS 1.4   6) AF 1.3

Date _____ Time _____

The base of a cylinder is circular. To find the area of the base of a cylinder, use the formula for finding the area of a circle.

> **Formula for the Area of a Circle**
>
> $$A = \pi * r^2$$
>
> where A is the area and r is the radius of the circle.

The formula for finding the volume of a cylinder is the same as the formula for finding the volume of a prism.

> **Formula for the Volume of a Cylinder**
>
> $$V = B * h$$
>
> where V is the volume of the cylinder, B is the area of the base, and h is the height of the cylinder.

Use the 2 cans you have been given.

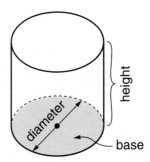

1. Measure the height of each can on the inside. Measure the diameter of the base of each can. Record your measurements (to the nearest tenth of a centimeter) in the table below.

2. Calculate the radius of the base of each can. Then use the formula to find the volume. Record the results in the table.

3. Record the capacity of each can in the table, in milliliters.

	Height (cm)	Diameter of Base (cm)	Radius of Base (cm)	Volume (cm³)	Capacity (mL)
Can #1					
Can #2					

4. Measure the liquid capacity of each can by filling the can with water. Then pour the water into a measuring cup. Keep track of the total amount of water you pour into the measuring cup.

Capacity of Can #1: _____ mL   Capacity of Can #2: _____ mL

Date _____ Time _____

Volume of Cylinders and Prisms

1. Find the volume of each cylinder.

a.

height = 8 in.

Area of base = 10 in²

Volume = _____ in³

b.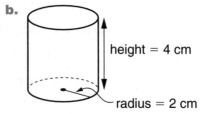

height = 4 cm

radius = 2 cm

Volume = _____ cm³

> **Reminder:** The same formula ($V = B * h$) may be used to find the volume of a prism and the volume of a cylinder.

2. Find the volume of each wastebasket. Then determine which wastebasket has the largest capacity and which one has the smallest.

a.

height = 16 in.

radius = 5 in.

Volume = _____ in³

b.

height = 14 in.

9 in.

9 in.

Volume = _____ in³

c.

height = 13 in.

radius = 6 in.

Volume = _____ in³

d.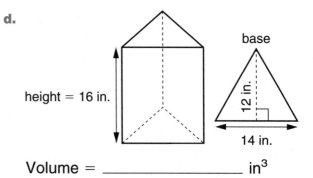

base

height = 16 in.

12 in.

14 in.

Volume = _____ in³

e. Which wastebasket has the largest capacity?   Wastebasket _____

Which wastebasket has the smallest capacity?   Wastebasket _____

376

LESSON 11·3 A Mental Calculation Strategy

When you multiply mentally, sometimes it is helpful to double one factor and halve the other factor.

Example 1: $45 * 12 = ?$

      Step 1 Double 45 and halve 12 $\longrightarrow 45 * 12 = 90 * 6$

      Step 2 Multiply 90 and 6 $\longrightarrow 90 * 6 = 540$

Example 2: $18 * 15 = ?$

      Step 1 Halve 18 and double 15 $\longrightarrow 18 * 15 = 9 * 30$

      Step 2 Multiply 9 and 30 $\longrightarrow 9 * 30 = 270$

Example 3: $75 * 28 = ?$

      Step 1 Double 75 to get 150 and halve 28 to get 14.

      Step 2 Double again to get 300 and halve again to get 7.

      Step 3 $75 * 28 = 300 * 7 = 2,100$

Use the doubling and halving strategy to calculate mentally. Solve the problems below.

1. $35 * 14 =$ _____

New number sentence:

_____

2. $16 * 25 =$ _____

New number sentence:

_____

3. $18 * 35 =$ _____

New number sentence:

_____

4. $15 * 44 =$ _____

New number sentence:

_____

5. $14 * 55 =$ _____

New number sentence:

_____

6. $75 * 24 =$ _____

New number sentence:

_____

New number sentence:

_____

LESSON 11·3 **Math Boxes**

---

1. Add or subtract.

   a. $-22 + 12 =$ _____

   b. $18 - (-4) =$ _____

   c. $-15 - (-8) =$ _____

   d. $-4 + (-17) =$ _____

   e. $-6 - (-28) =$ _____

SRB 92–94

---

2. Which parallelogram is not congruent to the other 3 parallelograms? Circle the best answer.

SRB 155

---

3. Mr. Ogindo's students took a survey of their favorite movie snacks. Complete the table. Then make a circle graph of the data.

Favorite Snack	Number of Students	Percent of Class
Popcorn	11	
Chocolate	5	
Soft drink	6	
Fruit chews	1	
Candy with nuts	2	
Total		

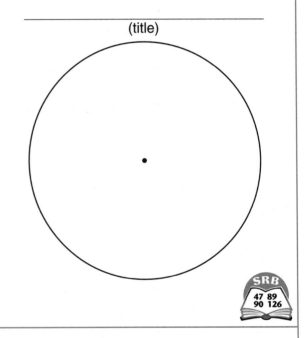

(title)

SRB 47 89 90 126

---

4. Solve.

   a. $\frac{3}{8}$ of 40 = _____

   b. $\frac{2}{3}$ of 120 = _____

   c. $\frac{4}{5}$ of 60 = _____

   d. $\frac{7}{9}$ of 54 = _____

   e. $\frac{5}{6}$ of 36 = _____

SRB 73

---

5. Write the prime factorization for 175.

_____

SRB 12

---

 1) NS 2.1   2) MG 2.1   3) SDAP 1.2
4) NS 2.5   5) NS 1.4

LESSON 11·4 Volume of Pyramids and Cones

1. To calculate the volume of any **prism** or **cylinder,** you multiply the area of the base by the height. How would you calculate the volume of a **pyramid** or a **cone?**

_____

_____

The Pyramid of Cheops is near Cairo, Egypt. It was built about 2600 B.C. It is a square pyramid. Each side of the square base is 756 feet long. Its height is 449.5 feet. The pyramid contains about 2,300,000 limestone blocks.

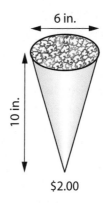

449.5 ft

756 ft

2. Calculate the volume of this pyramid. _____ ft³

3. What is the average volume of one limestone block?

_____ ft³

A movie theater sells popcorn in a box for $2.75. It also sells cones of popcorn for $2.00 each. The dimensions of the box and the cone are shown below.

7 in.

3 in.

9 in.

$2.75

6 in.

10 in.

$2.00

4. Calculate the volume of the box. _____ in³

5. Calculate the volume of the cone. _____ in³

Try This

6. Which is the better buy—the box or the cone of popcorn? Explain.

_____

_____

_____

Rugs and Fences: An Area and Perimeter Game

Materials
- ☐ 1 *Rugs and Fences* Area and Perimeter Deck (*Math Masters*, p. 498)
- ☐ 1 *Rugs and Fences* Polygon Deck (*Math Masters*, pp. 499 and 500)
- ☐ 1 *Rugs and Fences* Record Sheet (*Math Masters,* p. 501)

Players   2

Object of the game   To score the highest number of points by finding the area and perimeter of polygons.

Directions

1. Shuffle the Area and Perimeter Deck, and place it facedown.

2. Shuffle the Polygon Deck, and place it facedown next to the Area and Perimeter Deck.

3. Players take turns. At each turn, a player draws one card from each deck and places it faceup. The player finds the perimeter or area of the figure on the Polygon card as directed by the Area and Perimeter card.

   ◆ If a Player's Choice card is drawn, the player may choose to find either the area or the perimeter of the figure.

   ◆ If an Opponent's Choice card is drawn, the other player chooses whether the area or the perimeter of the figure will be found.

4. Players record their turns on the record sheet by writing the Polygon card number, by circling A (area) or P (perimeter), and then by writing the number model used to calculate the area or perimeter. The solution is the player's score for the round.

5. The player with the highest total score at the end of 8 rounds is the winner.

LESSON 11·4   **Math Boxes**

---

1. Solve.

   a. $\frac{1}{3}$ of 36 = _____

   b. $\frac{2}{5}$ of 75 = _____

   c. $\frac{3}{8}$ of 88 = _____

   d. $\frac{5}{6}$ of 30 = _____

   e. $\frac{2}{7}$ of 28 = _____

73

---

2. Find the volume of the solid.

Volume = $B * h$ where B is the area of the base and h is the height.

3 units

area of base 30 units^2

Volume = _____

197

---

3. Lilly earns $18.75 each day at her job. How much does she earn in 5 days?

Open sentence: _____

Solution: _____

38–40
243

---

4. Solve.

   a. 2 c = _____ fl oz

   b. 1 pt = _____ fl oz

   c. 1 qt = _____ fl oz

   d. 1 half-gal = _____ fl oz

   e. 1 gal = _____ fl oz

397

---

5. Make a factor tree to find the prime factorization of 32.

12

---

6. Jamar buys juice for the family. He buys eight 6-packs of juice boxes. His grandmother buys three more 6-packs. Which expression correctly represents how many juice boxes they bought? Circle the best answer.

   A. $(8 * 3) + 6$

   B. $6 * (8 * 3)$

   C. $6 * (8 + 3)$

219

LESSON 11·5   How to Calibrate a Bottle

Materials   ☐ 2-L plastic soft-drink bottle with the top cut off

☐ can or jar filled with about 2 L of water

☐ measuring cup   ☐ ruler

☐ scissors   ☐ paper

☐ tape

1. Fill the bottle with about 5 inches of water.

2. Cut a 1 in. by 6 in. strip of paper. Tape the strip to the outside of the bottle with one end at the bottle top and the other end below the water level.

3. Mark the paper strip at the water level. Write "0 mL" next to the mark.

4. Pour 100 milliliters of water into a measuring cup. Pour the water into the bottle. Mark the paper strip at the new water level, and write "100 mL."

5. Pour another 100 milliliters of water into the measuring cup. Pour it into the bottle, and mark the new water level "200 mL."

6. Repeat, adding 100 milliliters at a time until the bottle is filled to within an inch of the top.

7. Pour out the water until the water level in the bottle falls to the 0 mL mark.

   How would you use your calibrated bottle to find the volume of a rock?

   _____

   _____

   _____

Measurement and Geometry 1.0; Mathematical Reasoning 1.0

LESSON 11·5   Finding Volume by a Displacement Method

1. Check that the bottle is filled to the 0 mL level.
   Place several rocks in the bottle.

   Reminder: 1 mL = 1 cm^3

   a. What is the new level of the water in the bottle?   _____ mL

   b. What is the volume of the rocks?   _____ cm^3

   c. Does it matter whether the rocks are spread out or stacked?   _____

2. Your fist has nearly the same volume
   as your heart. Here is a way to find
   the approximate volume of your heart.
   Check that the bottle is filled to the
   0-mL level. Place a rubber band
   around your wrist, just below your
   wrist bone. Put your fist in the bottle
   until water reaches the rubber band.

   a. What is the new level of the water in the bottle?   _____ mL

   b. What is the volume of your fist?
      This is the approximate volume of your heart.   _____ cm^3

   c. Does it matter whether you make
      a fist or keep your hand open?   _____

3. Find the volumes of several other objects. For example, find the volume of a
   baseball, a golf ball, an orange, or an unopened can of soft drink. If the object
   floats, use a pencil to force it down. The object must be completely submerged
   before you read the water level.

Object	Volume of Water Object Displaces (mL)	Volume of Object (cm^3)

LESSON 11·5 Scanning the American Tour

Use the information in the American Tour section of the *Student Reference Book* to answer the following questions.

1. a. According to the National Facts table on page 391, what is the highest waterfall in the United States? _____

   b. If you were standing at the top of the cascades in the middle section, about how far would you be from the top of the falls? _____

   About how far would you be from the bottom of Lower Yosemite Fall? _____

2. a. According to the population density map on page 377, what is the average density for the entire United States? _____

   b. Write a number sentence to model how this average was calculated. (United States Population tables are on pages 374 and 375.) _____

   c. Name five states that have a population density more than twice the U.S. average?

   _____

3. Identify features and facts about your state.

   a. In what year did your state become a state? _____

   b. What are the highest and lowest points in your state? _____

   c. How does your state's population in 2000 compare with its population in 1900? _____

   d. What percent of your state's land area is forest? _____ Farmland? _____

   e. Describe a feature or a fact of your choice about your state.

   _____

4. According to the U.S. Highway Distances map on page 388, what is the highway distance between 2 of the largest U.S. cities?

   The distance between City 1 _____ and City 2 _____ is _____.

5. According to the information on pages 356 and 357, what has changed about the ratio of farm-workers to the size of the population fed by the farms in the United States in the last 100 years?

   _____

   _____

Statistics, Data Analysis, and Probability 1.0

LESSON 11·5 Math Boxes

---

1. Write each fraction in simplest form.

    a. $\dfrac{29}{3}$ = _____

    b. $\dfrac{43}{5}$ = _____

    c. $26\dfrac{34}{60}$ = _____

    d. $15\dfrac{9}{8}$ = _____

SRB 62 63

---

2. Find the volume of the prism.

> **Volume of a Triangular Box**
>
> Volume = Area of the base * height

9 cm

6 cm

4 cm

Volume = _____ cm³

SRB 197

---

3. Find the volume of the cylinder.

> **Volume of a Cylinder**
>
> Volume = Area of the base * height

7 in.

2 in.

Volume = _____ in³

SRB 198

---

4. Measure the base and the height of the triangle to the nearest centimeter.

    a. The base is about _____ cm.

    b. The height is about _____ cm.

    c. Find the area of the triangle to the nearest square centimeter.

> Area = $\dfrac{1}{2} * b * h$

Area: about _____ cm²

SRB 183 193

---

5. Solve.

    a.

One △ weighs as much as _____ Xs.

One ☐ weighs as much as _____ Xs.

    b.

One ☐ weighs as much as _____ marbles.

One △ weighs as much as _____ marbles.

SRB 228 229

LESSON 11·6 Capacity and Weight

Math Message

1. Describe the meaning of the picture, and explain how it can help you to convert among units of capacity (cups, pints, quarts, gallons, and so on).

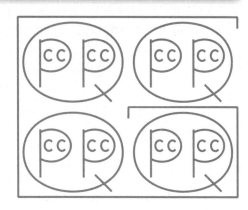

_____

_____

_____

_____

_____

_____

Use page 397 in the *Student Reference Book* as a reference, and solve the following.

2. 1 cup of dry (uncooked) rice weighs about _____ ounces.

3. Use the answer in Problem 2 to complete the following:

   a. 1 pint of rice weighs about _____ ounces.

   b. 1 quart of rice weighs about _____ ounces.

   c. 1 gallon of rice weighs about _____ ounces.

   d. 1 gallon of rice weighs about _____ pounds. (1 pound = 16 ounces)

4. On average, a family of 4 in Nepal eats about 110 pounds of rice per month.

   a. That's how many pounds in a year? _____

   b. How many gallons in a year? _____

5. On average, a family of 4 in the United States eats about 120 pounds of rice per year. That's about how many gallons per year? _____

6. On average, a family of 4 in Thailand eats about 3.5 gallons of rice in a week.

   a. That's about how many gallons per year? _____

   b. How many pounds per year? _____

Measurement and Geometry 1.4

Capacity and Weight *continued*

7. Find the capacity of the copy-paper carton shown at the right.

   _____ in³

9 in.

17 in.

11 in.

8. The container at the right is a half-gallon juice container with the top cut off so that $\frac{1}{2}$ gallon of juice fills it exactly.

   a. Find the volume of the half-gallon container.   _____ in³

   b. What is the volume of a one-gallon container?   _____ in³

$7\frac{1}{4}$ in.

4 in.

4 in.

9. On average, a family of 4 in Thailand eats about 182 gallons of rice per year. About how many copy-paper cartons will you need to hold this amount of rice? (*Hint:* First calculate how many gallons of rice will fill 1 copy-paper carton.)

   a. What is the capacity of 1 copy-paper carton?

   About _____ gallons

   b. How many copy-paper cartons will you need to hold 182 gallons of rice?

   About _____ cartons

10. How do your calculations compare to the class line plot of how many cartons would be needed to store all the rice a Thai family of 4 eats in a year?

   _____

   _____

11. Estimate about how many pounds a copy-paper carton full of rice weighs. Describe what you did to find your estimate.

   _____

   _____

   _____

   _____

LESSON 11·6 | **Math Boxes**

1. If a set has 48 objects, how many objects are there in …

a. $\frac{3}{8}$ of the set? _____

b. $\frac{8}{3}$ of the set? _____

c. $\frac{5}{6}$ of the set? _____

d. $\frac{7}{12}$ of the set? _____

e. $\frac{17}{16}$ of the set? _____

SRB 74

2. Solve.

 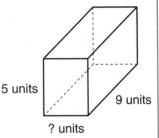

Volume of Prisms
$$V = B * h$$
where B is the area of the base and h is the height

5 units

9 units

? units

The volume of this prism is 180 units^3. What is the width of its base?

_____

SRB 197

3. Tito's grandmother bought him 2 packs of batteries for $4.98 each, and a game for $27.95. She now has $15.00. How much money did she have before shopping?

Open sentence:

_____

Solution: _____

SRB 219 243

4. Choose the best answer.

a. 1 half-gallon equals

◯ 1 quart   ◯ 2 quarts

◯ 2 pints   ◯ 4 quarts

b. 1 gallon equals

◯ 8 cups   ◯ 2 quarts

◯ 8 pints   ◯ 12 cups

SRB 397

5. Make a factor tree to find the prime factorization of 50.

SRB 12

6. Melissa baked 8 trays of 5 cookies each. She sold 3 plates of 12 cookies. Which expression correctly represents how many cookies she sold? Circle the best answer.

A. $(8 - 3) * 12$

B. $3 * 12$

C. $8 * 12$

SRB 219

1) NS 2.5   2) MG **1.3**   3) MR 1.1
4) MR 2.3   5) NS **1.4**   6) AF 1.3

LESSON 11·7 Surface Area

The **surface area** of a box is the sum of the areas of all 6 sides (faces) of the box.

1. Your class will find the dimensions of a cardboard box.

   a. Fill in the dimensions on the figure below.

   b. Find the area of each side of the box. Then find the total surface area.

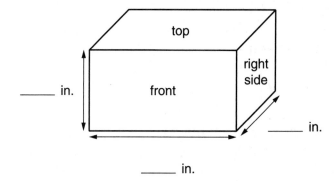

   Area of front = _____ in²

   Area of back = _____ in²

   Area of right side = _____ in²

   Area of left side = _____ in²

   Area of top = _____ in²

   Area of bottom = _____ in²
   _____

   Total surface area = _____ in²

2. *Think:* How would you find the **area** of the metal used to manufacture a can?

   a. How would you find the area of the top or bottom of the can?

   _____

   _____

   _____

   b. How would you find the area of the curved surface between the top and bottom of the can?

   _____

   _____

   _____

   c. Choose a can. Find the total area of the metal used to manufacture the can. Remember to include a unit for each area.

   Area of top = _____

   Area of bottom = _____

   Area of curved side surface = _____
   _____

   Total surface area = _____

LESSON 11·7

Surface Area *continued*

Formula for the Area of a Triangle

$$A = \frac{1}{2} * b * h$$

where *A* is the area of the triangle, *b* is the length of its base, and *h* is its height.

---

3. Use your model of a triangular prism.

    a. Find the dimensions of the triangular and rectangular faces. Then find the areas
        of these faces. Measure lengths to the nearest $\frac{1}{4}$ inch.

    base = _____ in.

    height = _____ in.

    Area = _____ in²

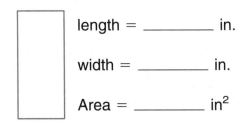

    length = _____ in.

    width = _____ in.

    Area = _____ in²

    b. Add the areas of the faces to find the total surface area.

    Area of 2 triangular bases = _____ in²

    Area of 3 rectangular sides = _____ in²

    Total surface area = _____ in²

4. Use your model of a square pyramid.

    a. Find the dimensions of the square and triangular faces. Then find the areas
        of these faces. Measure lengths to the nearest tenth of a centimeter.

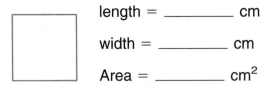

    length = _____ cm

    width = _____ cm

    Area = _____ cm²

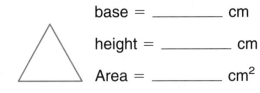

    base = _____ cm

    height = _____ cm

    Area = _____ cm²

    b. Add the areas of the faces to find the total surface area.

    Area of square base = _____ cm²

    Area of 4 triangular sides = _____ cm²

    Total surface area = _____ cm²

Measurement and Geometry ➊➋, 1.4; Mathematical Reasoning 3.2

LESSON 11·7   **Math Boxes**

---

1. Write each number in simplest form.

a. $\frac{80}{5} =$ _____

b. $\frac{53}{6} =$ _____

c. $8\frac{24}{48} =$ _____

d. $11\frac{38}{54} =$ _____

SRB
62 63

2. How are cylinders and cones alike?

_____

_____

SRB
147 148

---

3. Find the volume of the rectangular prism.

> **Volume of rectangular prism**
>
> $V = B * h$

1 cm
3 cm
4 cm

$V =$ _____ cm³

SRB
197

4. Find the area and perimeter of the rectangle.

7 cm

$3\frac{1}{2}$ cm

Area = _____ (unit)

Perimeter = _____ (unit)

SRB
186 189

---

5. Solve the pan-balance problems below.

a.

X X X X X
X X X X X X

One ◯ weighs as much as _____ Xs.

One ▢ weighs as much as _____ Xs.

b.

One △ weighs as much as _____ paper clips.

One ◯ weighs as much as _____ paper clips.

SRB
228 229

LESSON 11·8 **Math Boxes**

---

1. Solve.

   a. 34% of 200 _____

   b. 1% of 54 _____

   c. 10% of 623.9 _____

   d. 80% of 300 _____

   e. 15% of 30 _____

49 50

2. List all the factors for each number.

   a. 12 _____

   b. 20 _____

   c. 18 _____

   d. 36 _____

   e. 52 _____

10

---

3. Write each number in standard notation.

   a. $25^2 =$ _____

   b. $62^2 =$ _____

   c. $19^2 =$ _____

   d. $40^2 =$ _____

   e. $23^2 =$ _____

6

4. Make a factor tree to find the prime factorization of 28.

12

---

5. Write an equivalent fraction.

   a. $\frac{3}{5} =$ _____

   b. $\frac{4}{7} =$ _____

   c. $\frac{1}{9} =$ _____

   d. $\frac{2}{3} =$ _____

   e. $\frac{3}{4} =$ _____

59

6. Use your calculator to find the square root of each number.

   a. $\sqrt{361} =$ _____

   b. $\sqrt{2,704} =$ _____

   c. $\sqrt{8,649} =$ _____

   d. $\sqrt{4,356} =$ _____

271

---

1) NS 1.2   2) NS 1.4   3) NS 1.3
4) NS 1.4   5) NS 2.5   6) MR 1.0

LESSON 12·1 Factors

Math Message

1. Write all the pairs of factors whose product is 48. One pair has been done for you.

   48 = _6 * 8,_ _____

2. One way to write 36 as a product of factors is 2 * 18. Another way is 2 * 2 * 9. Write 36 as the product of the longest possible string of factors. Do not include 1 as a factor.

   _____

Factor Trees and Greatest Common Factors

One way to find all the prime factors of a number is to make a **factor tree.** First write the number. Underneath the number write any two factors whose product is that number. Then write factors of each of these factors. Continue until all the factors are prime numbers. Below are two factor trees for 45.

The **greatest common factor** of two whole numbers is the largest number that is a factor of both numbers.

Example: Find the greatest common factor of 24 and 60.

Step 1 List all the factors of 24: 1, 2, 3, 4, 6, 8, 12, and 24.

Step 2 List all the factors of 60: 1, 2, 3, 4, 5, 6, 10, 12, 15, 20, 30, and 60.

Step 3 1, 2, 3, 4, 6, and 12 are on both lists. They are **common factors.** 12 is the largest number, so it is the greatest common factor of 24 and 60.

3. Find the greatest common factor of 18 and 27.

   Factors of 18: _____

   Factors of 27: _____

   Greatest common factor: _____

LESSON 12·1 Factor Trees and Greatest Common Factors

Another way to find the greatest common factor of two numbers is to use prime factorization.

Example: Find the greatest common factor of 24 and 60.

Step 1 Make factor trees and write the prime factorization of each number.

$24 = 2 * 2 * 2 * 3$

$60 = 2 * 2 * 3 * 5$

Step 2 Circle pairs of common factors.

$$24 = 2 * 2 * 2 * 3$$
$$60 = 2 * 2 * 3 * 5$$

Step 3 Multiply *one* factor *in each pair* of circled factors.
The greatest common factor of 24 and 60 is $2 * 2 * 3$, or 12.

4. Make a factor tree for each number below, and write the prime factorization.

a.
10

b.
75

c.
90

10 = _____   75 = _____   90 = _____

Number Sense 1.4

LESSON 12·1 Factor Trees and Greatest Common Factors *cont.*

5. a. Which prime factor(s) do 10 and 75 have in common? _____

    b. What is the greatest common factor of 10 and 75? _____

6. a. Which prime factor(s) do 75 and 90 have in common? _____

    b. What is the greatest common factor of 75 and 90? _____

7. a. Which prime factor(s) do 10 and 90 have in common? _____

    b. What is the greatest common factor of 10 and 90? _____

8. Use the factor trees in Problem 4 to help you write each fraction below in simplest form. Divide the numerator and denominator by their greatest common factor.

    a. $\dfrac{10}{75} =$ _____   b. $\dfrac{75}{90} =$ _____

    c. $\dfrac{10}{90} =$ _____

9. What is the greatest common factor of 20 and 25? _____

    Write the fraction $\dfrac{20}{25}$ in simplest form. _____

10. Use the space below to draw factor trees. What is the greatest common factor of 1,260 and 1,350? _____

LESSON 12·1 Factor Trees and Least Common Multiples

The **least common multiple** of two numbers is the smallest number that is a multiple of both numbers.

Example: Find the least common multiple of 8 and 12.

Step 1 List the multiples of 8: 8, 16, 24, 32, 40, 48, 56, and so on.

Step 2 List the multiples of 12: 12, 24, 36, 48, 60, and so on.

Step 3 24 and 48 are in both lists. They are common multiples.
24 is the smallest number. It is the least common multiple for 8 and 12.
24 is also the smallest number that can be divided by both 8 and 12.

Another way to find the least common multiple for two numbers is to use prime factorization.

Example: Find the least common multiple of 8 and 12.

Step 1 Write the prime factorization of each number:

$$8 = 2 * 2 * 2 \qquad 12 = 2 * 2 * 3$$

Step 2 Circle pairs of common factors. Then cross out one factor in each pair as shown below.

$$8 = 2 * 2 * 2$$
$$12 = 2 * 2 * 3$$

Step 3 Multiply the factors that are not crossed out. The least common multiple of 8 and 12 is $2 * 2 * 2 * 3$, or 24.

1. Make factor trees and write the prime factorizations for each number.

   a.   15   **b.**   9   **c.**   30
                  / \   / \   / \

   15 = _____   9 = _____   30 = _____

2. What is the least common multiple of …

   a. 9 and 15? _____   **b.** 15 and 30? _____   **c.** 9 and 30? _____

Number Sense **1.4**

LESSON 12·1 **Math Boxes**

---

1. Solve.

   a. If 15 marbles are $\frac{3}{5}$ of the marbles in a bag, how many are in the bag? _____ marbles

   b. If 14 pennies are 7% of a pile of pennies, how many are in the pile? _____ pennies

   c. 75 students are absent today. This is 10% of the students enrolled at the school.

   How many students are enrolled at the school? _____ students

   d. Tyesha paid $90 for a new radio. It was on sale for $\frac{3}{4}$ of
   the regular price. What is the regular price of the radio? _____

SRB
75

---

2. A scooter is on sale for 30% of the list price. The sale price is $84. What is the list price?

   _____

SRB
52

3. Write > or <.

   a. 0.75 _____ $\frac{8}{9}$

   b. 0.2 _____ $\frac{1}{6}$

   c. $\frac{3}{7}$ _____ $\frac{4}{8}$

   d. $\frac{5}{9}$ _____ 0.9

   e. $\frac{6}{11}$ _____ $\frac{7}{12}$

SRB
9   89
90

---

4. Solve.

   a.

   One orange
   weighs as much as _____ Xs.

   One cube
   weighs as much as _____ Xs.

   b.

   One triangle
   weighs as much as _____ X.

   One paper clip
   weighs as much as _____ X.

SRB
228 229

LESSON 12·2 Probability

When a fair 6-sided die is rolled, each number from 1 to 6 has an equal chance of coming up. The numbers 1, 2, 3, 4, 5, and 6 are **equally likely.**

The spinner below is divided into 10 equal sections, so the chance of spinning the numbers 1–10 is **equally likely.** This does not mean that if you spin 10 times, each number from 1 to 10 will come up exactly once—2 might come up four times, and 10 might not come up at all. But if you spin many times (for example—1,000 times), each number is likely to come up about $\frac{1}{10}$ of the time. The **probability** of landing on 1 is $\frac{1}{10}$. The probability of landing on 2 is also $\frac{1}{10}$, and so on.

Example: What is the probability that the spinner at the right will land on an even number?

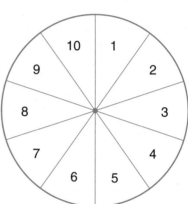

The spinner will land on an even number if it lands on 2, 4, 6, 8, or 10. Each of these even numbers is likely to come up $\frac{1}{10}$ of the time. The total probability that one of these even numbers will come up is found by adding:

$$\frac{1}{10} + \frac{1}{10} + \frac{1}{10} + \frac{1}{10} + \frac{1}{10} = \frac{5}{10}$$

Lands on: 2   4   6   8   10

The probability of landing on an even number is $\frac{5}{10}$.

Find the probability of each of the following for this spinner.

1. The spinner lands on an odd number. _____

2. The spinner lands on a number less than 7. _____

3. The spinner lands on a multiple of 3. _____

4. The spinner lands on a number that is a factor of 12. _____

5. The spinner lands on the greatest common factor of 4 and 6. _____

6. The spinner lands on a prime number. _____

7. The spinner lands on a number that is *not* a prime number. _____

Statistics, Data Analysis, and Probability 1.3

LESSON 12·2

The Multiplication Counting Principle and Tree Diagrams

Multiplication Counting Principle

Suppose you can make a first choice in *m* ways and a second choice in *n* ways.
Then there are *m* ∗ *n* ways of making the first choice followed by the second choice.
Three or more choices can be counted in the same way, by multiplying.

A school cafeteria offers these choices for lunch:

Main course: chili or hamburger

Drink: milk or juice

Dessert: apple or cake

1. **a.** How many different ways can a student choose one main course, one drink, and
one dessert? Use the Multiplication Counting Principle.

_____ ∗ _____ ∗ _____

(ways to choose   (ways to choose   (ways to choose
a main course)   a drink)   a dessert)

b. Number of different combinations of foods for lunch: _____

2. Draw a **tree diagram** to show all possible ways to select foods for lunch.

Main course: _____   _____

Drink: _____   _____   _____   _____

Dessert: _____ _____ _____ _____ _____ _____ _____ _____

3. **a.** Do you think that all of the combinations of foods for lunch are equally likely? _____

b. Explain your answer. _____

_____

_____

LESSON 12·2 Tree Diagrams and Probability

José has 3 clean shirts (red, blue, and yellow) and 2 clean pairs of pants (tan and black). He grabs a shirt and a pair of pants without looking.

1. Complete the tree diagram to show all possible ways that José can choose a shirt and a pair of pants.

   Shirts: _____   _____   _____

   Pants: _____ _____   _____ _____   _____ _____

2. List all possible combinations of shirts and pants. One has been done for you.

   red and black, _____

   _____

3. How many different combinations of shirts and pants are there? _____ combinations

4. Are all the shirt-pants combinations equally likely? _____

5. What is the probability that José will grab the following?

   a. the blue shirt _____

   b. the blue shirt and the black pants _____

   c. the tan pants _____

   d. a shirt that is *not* yellow _____

   e. the tan pants and a shirt that is *not* yellow _____

Mathematical Reasoning 2.3

LESSON 12·2 Tree Diagrams and Probability *continued*

Mr. Jackson travels to and from work by train. Trains to work leave at 6:00, 7:00, 8:00, and 9:00 A.M. Trains from work leave at 3:00, 4:00, and 5:00 P.M.

Mr. Jackson is equally likely to select any 1 of the 4 morning trains to go to work.

He is equally likely to select any of the 3 afternoon trains to go home from work.

To work: 6   7   8   9 A.M.

From work: 3 4 5 3 4 5 3 4 5 3 4 5 P.M.

1. In how many different ways can
   Mr. Jackson take trains to and from work? _____ different ways

2. Are these ways equally likely? _____

3. What is the probability of each of the following?

   a. Mr. Jackson takes the 7:00 A.M. train to work. _____

   b. He returns home on the 4:00 P.M. train. _____

   c. He takes the 7:00 A.M. train to work and returns on the 4:00 P.M. train. _____

   d. He leaves on the 9:00 A.M. train and returns on the 5:00 P.M. train. _____

   e. He leaves for work before 9:00 A.M. _____

   f. He leaves for work at 6:00 A.M. or 7:00 A.M. and returns at 3:00 P.M. _____

   g. He returns home, but *not* on the 5:00 P.M. train. _____

   h. He returns home 9 hours after taking the train to go to work. _____

LESSON 12·2   **Rate Number Stories**

1. Mica reads about 44 pages in an hour.
   About how many pages will she read in $2\frac{3}{4}$ hour? _____ pages

   Explain how you found your answer. _____

   _____

   _____

   _____

   If Mica starts reading a 230-page book at 3:30 P.M., and she reads straight
   through the book without stopping, about what time will Mica finish the book? _____

   Explain how you found your answer. _____

   _____

   _____

   _____

   _____

   _____

2. Tyree and Jake built a tower of centimeter cubes. The bottom floor of the tower is
   rectangular. It is 5 cubes wide and 10 cubes long. The completed tower is the
   shape of a rectangular prism. They began building at 2 P.M. They built for about
   1 hour. They used approximately 200 cubes every 10 minutes.

   How tall was the final tower? _____
                                      (unit)

   Explain how you found your answer. _____

   _____

   _____

   _____

   _____

   _____

Mathematical Reasoning 1.1

Date _____ Time _____

---

1. Divide mentally.

   a. 382 / 7 → _____

   b. 796 / 5 → _____

   c. 499 / 4 → _____

   d. 283 ÷ 6 → _____

   e. 1,625 ÷ 8 → _____

SRB 22–24

2. Draw a rectangle whose perimeter is the same as the perimeter of the rectangle shown, but whose sides are not the same length as those shown.

3.5 cm

2.5 cm

What is the area of the figure you've drawn?

_____

SRB 142 186 189

---

3. Multiply. Show your work.

   a.   55
       * 37
       ―――

   b.   92
       * 74
       ―――

   c.   318
       * 64
       ―――

SRB 19 20

---

4. **a.** Measure the radius of the circle in centimeters. _____

   b. Find the area to the nearest cm^2 and the circumference to the nearest cm.

      Area = π * radius^2

      Circumference = π * diameter

      The area is about _____.

      The circumference is about _____.

SRB 153

LESSON 12·3   Ratios

Ratios can be expressed in many ways. All of the following are statements of ratios:

◆ It is estimated that by the year 2020 there will be 5 times as many people 100 years old or older than there were in 1990.

◆ Elementary school students make up about 14% of the U.S. population.

◆ On an average evening, about $\frac{1}{3}$ of the U.S. population watches TV.

◆ The chances of winning a lottery can be less than 1 in 1,000,000.

◆ A common scale for dollhouses is 1 inch to 12 inches.

A **ratio** uses division to compare two counts or measures having the same unit. Ratios can be stated or written in a variety of ways. Sometimes a ratio is easier to understand or will make more sense if it is rewritten in another form.

Example: In a group of ten students, eight students are right-handed and two are left-handed. The ratio of left-handed students to all students can be expressed in the following ways:

◆ With words: Two out of the ten students are left-handed.
Two in ten students are left-handed.
The ratio of left-handed students to all students is two to ten.

◆ With a fraction: $\frac{2}{10}$, or $\frac{1}{5}$ of the students are left-handed.

◆ With a percent: 20% of the students are left-handed.

◆ With a colon between the two numbers being compared:
The ratio of left-handed students to all students is 2:10 (two to ten).

Math Message

Express the ratio of right-handed students to all students in the example above.

1. With words: _____ students are right-handed.

2. With a fraction: _____ of the students are right-handed.

3. With a percent: _____ of the students are right-handed.

4. With a colon: The ratio of right-handed students to all students is _____.

Number Sense 1.2; Statistics, Data Analysis, and Probability 1.3

LESSON 12·3   Using Ratios to Examine a Trend

1. a. According to the table on page 356 of the *Student Reference Book,* has the ratio of farmers to all working people increased or decreased since 1900?

   _____

   b. Why do you think this has happened? _____

   _____

   _____

2. a. Has the ratio of engineers to all working people increased or decreased since 1900?

   _____

   b. Why do you think this has happened? _____

   _____

   _____

3. a. How has the ratio of photographers to all working people changed since 1900?

   _____

   b. Why do you think this has happened? _____

   _____

   _____

4. About how many farmers were there …

   a. in 1900? _____

   b. in 2000? _____

5. About how many photographers were there …

   a. in 1900? _____

   b. in 2000? _____

LESSON 12·3 10 Times

Have you ever heard or used expressions such as "10 times more," "10 times as many," "10 times less," or "$\frac{1}{10}$ as many?" These are **ratio comparisons.** Be sure to use expressions like these with caution. Increasing or reducing something by a factor of 10 makes a big difference!

Scientists call a difference of 10 times a **magnitude,** and they believe that the world as we know it changes drastically when something is increased or decreased by a magnitude.

Example: A person can jog about 5 miles per hour. A car can travel 10 times faster than that, or 50 miles per hour. A plane can travel 10 times faster than that, or 500 miles per hour. Each magnitude increase in travel speed has had a great effect on our lives.

Complete the following table. Then add two of your own events or items to the table.

Event or Item	Current Measure or Count	10 Times More	10 Times Less ($\frac{1}{10}$ as much)
Length of math class			
Number of students in math class			
Length of your stride			

▶ **Number Sense 1.2; Mathematical Reasoning 1.1**

LESSON 12·3 **Math Boxes**

---

1. Marvin missed $\frac{1}{8}$ of the 24 shots he took in a basketball game against the Rams.

   a. What fraction of the shots did he make? _____

   b. How many shots did he miss? _____

   c. How many shots did he make? _____

   d. What percent of his shots did he make? _____

74

---

2. A backpack is on sale for 20% of the list price. The sale price is $15.95.

   What is the list price? _____

   52

3. Write > or <.

   a. $\frac{7}{8}$ _____ $\frac{9}{10}$

   b. $\frac{4}{5}$ _____ 0.89

   c. $\frac{2}{3}$ _____ $\frac{5}{8}$

   d. 0.37 _____ $\frac{2}{5}$

   e. $\frac{9}{6}$ _____ 1.05

   9 89
   90

---

4. Solve.

   a.

   One banana
   weighs as much as ____ Ps.

   One cube
   weighs as much as ____ Ps.

   b.

   One cube
   weighs as much as ____ marbles.

   One X
   weighs as much as ____ marbles.

   228 229

LESSON 12·4 Comparing Parts to Wholes

A **ratio** is a comparison. Some ratios compare part of a collection of things to the total number of things in the collection. For example, the statement "1 out of 6 students in the class is absent" compares the number of students absent to the total number of students in the class. Another way to express this ratio is to say, "For every 6 students enrolled in the class, 1 student is absent" or "$\frac{1}{6}$ of the students in the class are absent."

If you know the total number of students in the class, you can use this ratio to find the number of students who are absent. For example, if there are 12 students in the class, then $\frac{1}{6}$ of 12, or 2 of the students are absent. If there are 18 students in the class, then $\frac{1}{6}$ of 18, or 3 students are absent.

If you know the number of students who are absent, you can also use this ratio to find the total number of students in the class. For example, if 5 students are absent, there must be a total of 6 ∗ 5, or 30 students in the class.

Use the Square Tiles from *Math Journal 2,* Activity Sheet 7 to model and solve the following ratio problems.

1. Place 28 tiles on your desk so that 3 out of 4 tiles are white and the rest are shaded.

   How many tiles are white? _____   How many tiles are shaded? _____

   Draw your tile model.

2. Place 30 tiles on your desk so that 4 out of 5 tiles are white and the rest are shaded.

   How many tiles are white? _____   How many tiles are shaded? _____

3. Place 7 shaded tiles on your desk. Add some tiles so that 1 out of
   3 tiles is shaded and the rest are white. How many tiles are there in all? _____

   Draw your tile model.

4. Place 25 white tiles on your desk. Add some tiles so that 5 out of
   8 tiles are white and the rest are shaded. How many tiles are there in all? _____

Mathematical Reasoning 2.3

LESSON 12·4 Ratio Number Stories

Use your tiles to model and solve the number stories below.

1. Take 32 tiles. If 6 out of 8 are white, how many are white? _____

2. Take 15 tiles. If 6 out of 9 are white, how many are white? _____

3. Place 24 tiles on your desk so that 8 are white and the rest are shaded.

   One out of _____ tiles is white.

4. Place 18 tiles on your desk so that 12 are white and the rest are shaded.

   _____ out of 3 tiles are white.

5. It rained 2 out of 5 days in the month of April.

   On how many days did it rain that month? _____

6. For every 4 times John was at bat, he got 1 hit.

   If he got 7 hits, how many times did he bat? _____

7. There are 20 students in Mrs. Kahlid's fifth-grade class. Two out of 8 students have no brothers or sisters. How many students have no brothers or sisters?

   _____

8. Rema eats 2 eggs twice a week. How many eggs will she eat in the month of February? _____

   How many weeks will it take her to eat 32 eggs? _____

9. David took a survey of people's favorite flavors of ice cream. Of the people he surveyed, 2 out of 5 said that they like fudge swirl best, 1 out of 8 chose vanilla, 3 out of 10 chose maple walnut, and the rest chose another flavor.

   a. If 16 people said fudge swirl is their favorite flavor, how many people took part in David's survey? _____

   b. If 80 people participated in David's survey, how many preferred a flavor that is not fudge swirl, vanilla, or maple walnut?

   _____

◀ **Mathematical Reasoning 2.3**

LESSON 12·4   Calculating Choices

1. The ice-cream shop has 3 flavors of ice cream and 5 different toppings.

   a. Use the Multiplication Counting Principle to calculate the total
      number of choices for one flavor of ice cream and one topping. _____

   b. Draw a tree diagram to show the possible combinations.

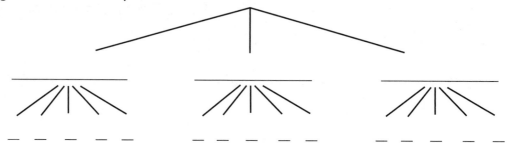

2. U.S. radio station call letters must start with W or K—as in WNIB or KYFM.

   a. How many choices are there for the first letter? _____

      The second letter? _____   The third letter? _____

      The last letter? _____

   b. How many different 4-letter combinations are possible?

      _____

   c. Would you use a tree diagram to solve this problem? Explain why or why not.

      _____

      _____

      _____

3. There are 4 number cards: 1, 2, 3, and 4.

   a. Calculate the total number of possible combinations for two cards if you mix the
      cards, draw one card without looking, replace the drawn card, remix the cards,
      and draw one card again. _____

   b. Calculate the total number of possible combinations for cards if you mix the
      cards, draw one card without looking and put it aside, remix the cards, and
      draw one card again. _____

Mathematical Reasoning 2.3

LESSON 12·4 | **Math Boxes**

---

1. Divide mentally.

a. 472 ÷ 5 → _____

b. 389 / 6 → _____

c. 729 / 8 → _____

d. 543 ÷ 4 → _____

e. 580 ÷ 9 → _____

SRB 22–24

---

2. a. A rectangle has an area of 8 cm². Draw and label the sides of the rectangle.

b. What is the perimeter of the rectangle you've drawn? _____

SRB 142 186 189

---

3. Multiply. Use an algorithm of your choice.

a.
```
   26
 * 32
 ____
```

b.
```
   71
 * 58
 ____
```

c.
```
   93
 * 47
 ____
```

SRB 19

---

4. a. Draw a circle with a radius of 2.5 centimeters.

b. What is the area of this circle to the nearest centimeter?

Area = π * radius²

About _____
           (unit)

SRB 153

LESSON 12·5   More Ratio Number Stories

You can solve ratio number stories by first writing a number model for the story.

Example: Sidney missed 2 out of 9 problems on the math test. There were 36 problems on the test. How many problems did he miss?

◆ Write a number model: $\frac{\text{(missed)}}{\text{(total)}}\ \frac{2}{9} = \frac{\square}{36}$

◆ Find the missing number.

Think: *9 times what number equals 36?* $9 * 4 = 36$

Multiply the numerator, 2, by this number: $2 * 4 = 8$

$\frac{\text{(missed)}}{\text{(total)}}\ \frac{2 * 4}{9 * 4} = \frac{8}{36}$

◆ Answer: Sidney missed 8 out of 36 problems.

Write a number model for each problem. Then solve the problem.

1. Of the 42 animals in the Children's Zoo, 3 out of 7 are mammals. How many mammals are in the Children's Zoo?

   Number model: _____ Answer: _____

   (unit)

2. Five out of 8 students at Kenwood School play an instrument. There are 224 students at the school. How many students play an instrument?

   Number model: _____ Answer: _____

   (unit)

3. Mr. Lopez sells subscriptions to a magazine. Each subscription costs $18. For each subscription he sells, he earns $8. One week, he sold $198 worth of subscriptions. How much did he earn?

   Number model: _____ Answer: _____

Algebra and Functions **1.2**

**LESSON
12·5**   **More Ratio Number Stories** *continued*

4. Make up a ratio number story. Ask your partner to solve it.

_____

_____

_____

Number model: _____

Answer: _____

Find the missing number.

5. $\dfrac{1}{3} = \dfrac{x}{39}$

   $x =$ _____

6. $\dfrac{3}{4} = \dfrac{21}{y}$

   $y =$ _____

7. $\dfrac{7}{8} = \dfrac{f}{56}$

   $f =$ _____

8. $\dfrac{1}{5} = \dfrac{13}{n}$

   $n =$ _____

9. $\dfrac{5}{6} = \dfrac{m}{42}$

   $m =$ _____

10. $\dfrac{9}{25} = \dfrac{s}{100}$

    $s =$ _____

11. There are 48 students in the fifth grade at Robert's school. Three out of
8 fifth graders read two books last month. One out of 3 students read
just one book. The rest of the students read no books at all.

How many books in all did the fifth graders read last month? _____
(unit)

Explain what you did to find the answer.

_____

_____

_____

_____

_____

Algebra and Functions 1.2

LESSON 12·5   Naming Angle Measures

1. Use your knowledge of angles to complete the table.

Angle Name	Angle Reference	Angle Measure
acute	Less than a quarter turn	$< 90°$
right		
obtuse		
straight		
reflex angle		
Sum of measures of adjacent angles		

2. Describe your method for remembering the difference between an acute angle and an obtuse angle.

_____

_____

_____

Measurement and Geometry 2.1

Math Boxes

---

1. Rewrite each fraction pair with common denominators.

a. $\frac{1}{3}$ and $\frac{1}{2}$ _____

b. $\frac{3}{4}$ and $\frac{2}{5}$ _____

c. $\frac{2}{8}$ and $\frac{9}{12}$ _____

SRB
65

---

2. List the factors of 142.

_____

SRB
10

---

3. Estimate the answer for each problem. Then solve the problem.

	Estimate	Solution
a. 302 * 57	_____	_____
b. 599 * 9	_____	_____
c. 701 * 97	_____	_____
d. 498 * 501	_____	_____

SRB
247

---

4. There are 270 students in the soccer league. Two out of three students are boys. How many students are boys?

_____

SRB
108 109

---

5. Complete the table. Graph the data and connect the points with line segments.

Maryanne earns $12 per hour.

Rule:
Earnings =
12 * number of hours

Hours	Earnings
2	
4	
	60
	84
9	

Maryanne's Earnings

Earnings ($)

Number of Hours

SRB
124 231 232

LESSON 12·6   The Heart

The heart is an organ in your body that pumps blood through your blood vessels. **Heart rate** is the rate at which your heart pumps blood. It is usually expressed as the number of heartbeats per minute. With each heartbeat, the arteries stretch and then return to their original size. This throbbing of the arteries is called the **pulse.** The **pulse rate** is the same as the heart rate.

You can feel your pulse along your wrist, near the bone and below the thumb. You can also feel it in your neck. Run your index and middle fingers from your ear, past the curve of your jaw, and press them into the soft part of your neck just below your jaw.

My Heart Rate

Feel your pulse and count the number of heartbeats in 15 seconds. Your partner can time you with a watch or the classroom clock. Do this several times, until you are sure that your count is accurate.

1. About how many times does your heart beat in 15 seconds? _____

2. Use this rate to complete the table.

About how many times your heart beats . . .	
in 1 minute	
in 1 hour	
in 1 day	
in 1 year	

3. Your fist and your heart are about the same size. Measure your fist with your ruler. Record the results.

   My heart is about _____ inches wide and _____ inches long.

4. A person's heart weighs about 1 ounce per 12 pounds of body weight.

   Circle how much your heart weighs.

   Less than 15 ounces   About 15 ounces   More than 15 ounces

LESSON 12·6 **Math Boxes**

1. Plot and label the ordered number pairs on the grid.

M: (2,5)

N: (−2,1)

O: (−3,−4)

P: (−4,3)

Q: (6,−2)

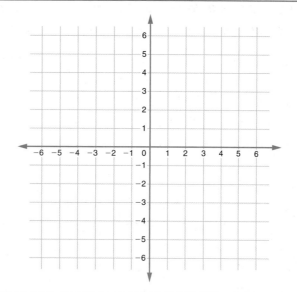

SRB
208

---

2. Find the fraction equivalent to $\frac{35}{84}$.

Circle the best answer.

A. $\frac{3}{5}$

B. $\frac{3}{4}$

C. $\frac{5}{6}$

D. $\frac{5}{12}$

SRB
59

3. What is the measure of angle A? Do *not* use a protractor.

∠A = _____

SRB
207

---

4. Name two equivalent fractions for each fraction below.

a. $\frac{7}{8}$ = _____

b. $\frac{3}{10}$ = _____

c. $\frac{6}{7}$ = _____

d. $\frac{1}{6}$ = _____

e. $\frac{12}{5}$ = _____

SRB
59

5. Write > or <.

a. 50% _____ $\frac{2}{3}$

b. 620 − 80 _____ 30 * 40

c. $\frac{7}{8}$ _____ $\frac{1}{4} + \frac{2}{4}$

d. 20 * 19 _____ 20^2

e. 0.35 + 0.25 _____ $\frac{1}{8} + \frac{1}{8}$

SRB
9 89
90

LESSON 12·7   Exercise Your Heart

Exercise increases the rate at which a person's heart beats. Very strenuous exercise can double the heart rate.

Work with a partner to find out how exercise affects your heart rate.

Step-ups	Heartbeats per 15 Seconds
0	
5	
10	
15	
20	
25	

1. Sit quietly for a minute. Then have your partner time you for 15 seconds while you take your pulse. Record the number of heartbeats in the first row of the table at the right.

2. Step up onto and down from a chair 5 times without stopping. Maintain your balance each time you step up or down. As soon as you finish, take your pulse for 15 seconds while your partner times you. Record the number of heartbeats in the second row of the table.

3. Sit quietly. While you are resting, your partner can do 5 step-ups, and you can time your partner.

4. When your pulse is almost back to normal, step up onto and down from the chair 10 times. Record the number of heartbeats in 15 seconds in the third row of the table. Then rest while your partner does 10 step-ups.

5. Repeat the procedure for 15, 20, and 25 step-ups.

6. Why is it important that all students step up at the same rate?

_____

_____

_____

_____

Algebra and Functions 1.1, **1.5**; Statistics, Data analysis, and Probability 1.0, **1.4**

LESSON 12·7 My Heart-Rate Profile

1. Make a line graph of the data in your table on journal page 418.

2. Make a prediction: What will your heart rate be if you do 30 step-ups?

About _____ heartbeats in 15 seconds

3. When you exercise, you must be careful not to put too much stress on your heart. Exercise experts often recommend a target heart rate to reach during exercise. The target heart rate varies, depending on a person's age and health, but the following rule is sometimes used.

Target heart rate during exercise:

Subtract your age from 220. Multiply the result by 2. Then divide by 3.

The result is the target number of heartbeats per minute.

a. According to this rule, what is your target heart rate during exercise?

About _____ heartbeats per minute

b. That is about how many heartbeats in 15 seconds?

About _____ heartbeats

LESSON 12·7 My Class's Heart-Rate Profile

1. Complete the table.

Class Landmarks: Number of Heartbeats per 15 Seconds				
Number of Step-ups	Maximum	Minimum	Range	Median
0				
5				
10				
15				
20				
25				

2. Make a line graph of the medians on the grid on journal page 419. Use a colored pencil or crayon. Label this line Class Profile. Label the other line My Own Profile.

3. Compare your personal profile to the class profile.

_____

_____

_____

_____

_____

_____

Statistics, Data Analysis, and Probability 1.0, 1.1

LESSON
12·7
Solving Pan-Balance Problems

Solve.

1.

One circle
weighs as much as ____ Xs.

One square
weighs as much as ____ circle.

2.

One cube
weighs as much as ____ balls.

One ball
weighs as much as ____ X.

3.

One circle
weighs as much as ____ triangles.

One square
weighs as much as ____ triangles.

4.

One X weighs as much as ____ Ys.

One Y weighs as much as ____ Zs.

**LESSON
12·7**   **Math Boxes**

---

1. Rewrite each fraction pair with common denominators.

   a. $\frac{2}{3}$ and $\frac{3}{5}$ _____

   b. $\frac{3}{7}$ and $\frac{9}{10}$ _____

   c. $\frac{3}{8}$ and $\frac{18}{24}$ _____

2. List all the factors of 165.

   _____

---

3. Estimate the answer for each problem. Then solve the problem.

	Estimate	Solution
a. 60.3 * 71	_____	_____
b. 29 * 0.8	_____	_____
c. 48 * 2.02	_____	_____
d. 2.2 * 550	_____	_____

4. Elise has 96 coins in her collection. One out of four is from a foreign country. How many coins are from a foreign country?

   _____

---

5. Fran reads at a rate of 50 pages per hour.
   Complete the table. Graph the data and connect the points with line segments.

   Rule: pages = 50 * hours

Hours	Pages
1	50
2	
	150
	250
7	

   Fran's Reading Rate

   Number of Hours

1) NS 2.5   2) MR 1.1   3) MR 2.5
4) MR 2.2   5) AF 1.5

LESSON 12·8   Review of Ratios

1. What is the ratio of the length of line segment *AB* to the length of line segment *CD*?

A ————— B   C ————————————— D

$1\frac{1}{2}$ in.   3 in.

2. Circle the pair of line segments whose lengths have the same ratio as *AB* to *CD* in Problem 1.

a.
E F   G ————————————— H

1 cm   5 cm

b.
I ————— J   K ——————— L

$\frac{3}{4}$ in. $1\frac{1}{2}$ in.

c.
M ——————————————————— N   O ——————————————— P

10 cm   6 cm

3. There are 13 boys and 15 girls in a group.
What fractional part of the group is boys? _____

4. Problem 3 was given to groups of 13-year-olds, 17-year-olds, and adults. The answers and the percent of each group that gave those particular answers are shown in the table below.

Answers	13-Year-Olds	17-Year-Olds	Adults
$\frac{13}{28}$	20%	36%	25%
$\frac{13}{28}$ written as a decimal	0%	0%	1%
$\frac{13}{15}$ or 0.86	17%	17%	15%
$\frac{15}{28}$	2%	2%	3%
Other incorrect answers	44%	29%	35%
Don't know	12%	13%	20%
No answer	5%	3%	1%

a. What mistake was made by the people who gave the answer $\frac{15}{28}$?

_____

_____

b. What mistake was made by the people who gave the answer $\frac{13}{15}$?

_____

_____

LESSON 12·8 The Heart Pump

Your heart is the strongest muscle in your body. It needs to be because it never rests. Every day of your life, 24 hours a day, your heart pumps blood throughout your body. The blood carries the **nutrients** and **oxygen** your body needs to function.

You breathe oxygen into your lungs. The oxygen passes from your lungs into your bloodstream. As your heart pumps blood throughout your body, the oxygen is deposited in the cells of your body and is replaced by waste products (mainly **carbon dioxide**). The blood carries the carbon dioxide back to your lungs, which get rid of the carbon dioxide when you exhale. The carbon dioxide is replaced by oxygen, and the cycle begins again.

The amount of blood the heart pumps in 1 minute is called the **cardiac output.** To find your cardiac output, you need to know your **heart rate** and the average amount of blood your heart pumps with each heartbeat. Cardiac output is calculated as follows:

Cardiac output = (amount of blood pumped per heartbeat) ∗ (heart rate)

On average, the heart of a fifth grader pumps about 1.6 fluid ounces of blood with each heartbeat. If your heart beats about 90 times per minute, then your heart pumps about 1.6 ∗ 90, or 144 fluid ounces of blood per minute. Your cardiac output would be about 144 fluid ounces, or $1\frac{1}{8}$ gallons of blood per minute. That's about 65 gallons of blood per hour. Imagine having to do this much work, around the clock, every day of your life! Can you see why your heart needs to be very strong?

A person's normal heart rate decreases with age. A newborn's heart rate can be as high as 110 to 160 beats per minute. For 10-year-olds, it is around 90 beats per minute; for adults, it is between 70 and 80 beats per minute. It is not unusual for older people's hearts to beat as few as 50 to 65 times per minute.

Because cardiac output depends on a person's heart rate, it is not the same at all times. The more often the heart beats in 1 minute, the more blood is pumped throughout the body.

Exercise helps your heart grow larger and stronger. The larger and stronger your heart is, the more blood it can pump with each heartbeat. A stronger heart needs fewer heartbeats to pump the same amount of blood. This puts less of a strain on the heart.

Mathematical Reasoning 1.1

LESSON 12·8 The Heart Pump *continued*

Pretend that your heart has been pumping the same amount of blood all of your life—so far, about 65 gallons of blood per hour.

1. **a.** At that rate, about how many gallons of blood would your heart pump per day?

   About _____ gallons

   b. About how many gallons per year? About _____ gallons

2. At that rate, about how many gallons would it have pumped from the time you were born to your last birthday?

   About _____ gallons

3. Heart rate and cardiac output increase with exercise. Look at the table on journal page 418. Find the number of heartbeats in 15 seconds when you are at rest and the number of heartbeats after 25 step-ups. Record them below.

   a. Heartbeats in 15 seconds at rest: _____

   b. Heartbeats in 15 seconds after 25 step-ups: _____

   Now figure out the number of heartbeats in 1 minute.

   c. Heartbeats in 1 minute at rest: _____

   d. Heartbeats in 1 minute after 25 step-ups: _____

4. If your heart pumps about 1.6 fluid ounces of blood per heartbeat, about how much blood does it pump in 1 minute when you are at rest?

   About _____ fl oz

5. A gallon is equal to 128 fluid ounces. About how many gallons of blood does your heart pump in 1 minute when you are at rest?

   About _____ gallon(s)

6. **a.** Use your answer to Problem 5 above to find about how many fluid ounces of blood your heart would pump in 1 minute after 25 step-ups.

   About _____ fl oz

   b. About how many gallons? About _____ gallon(s)

Mathematical Reasoning 1.1

LESSON 12·8 **Math Boxes**

---

1. Plot and label the ordered number pairs on the grid.

E: (−2,5)

F: (3,4)

G: (−2,−4)

H: (−1,0)

I: (5,−1)

J: (4,4)

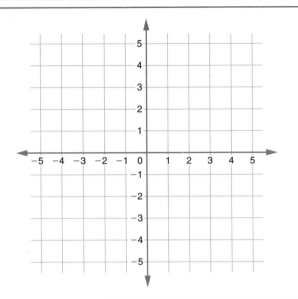

SRB 208

---

2. $\boxed{} = \frac{45}{54}$

Circle the best answer.

A. $\frac{5}{8}$

B. $\frac{4}{5}$

C. $\frac{5}{6}$

D. $\frac{3}{5}$

SRB 59

---

3. What is the measure of angle S? Do *not* use a protractor.

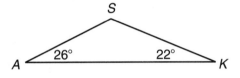

$\angle S =$ _____

SRB 207

---

4. Name two equivalent fractions for each fraction below.

a. $\frac{1}{3} =$ _____

b. $\frac{3}{8} =$ _____

c. $\frac{2}{7} =$ _____

d. $\frac{9}{4} =$ _____

e. $\frac{5}{3} =$ _____

SRB 59

---

5. Write > or <.

a. $15 + 28$ _____ 10^2

b. $40 + 40$ _____ $3 * 30$

c. $\frac{1}{2} + \frac{1}{2}$ _____ $\frac{3}{4}$

d. $\frac{19}{20}$ _____ $0.6 + 0.3$

e. $55 \div 5$ _____ $120 \div 12$

SRB 9 89 90

---

1) AF **1.4**   2) NS 2.5   3) MG **2.2**
4) NS **1.2**   5) NS **1.5**

LESSON 12·9 Math Boxes

---

1. One square weighs as much as _____ ounces.

\ 3 □ + 14 ounces /   \ 23 ounces /

SRB
228 229

---

2. The area of the cover of the dictionary is

about _____.
   (unit)

$9\frac{5}{8}$ in.

Dictionary of American English

$7\frac{3}{4}$ in.

SRB
189

---

3. Write a fraction or a mixed number for each of the following.

a. 5 minutes = _____ hour

b. 20 minutes = _____ hour

c. 35 minutes = _____ hour

d. 10 minutes = _____ hour

e. 55 minutes = _____ hour

SRB
397

---

4. Multiply.

a. $\frac{7}{8} * \frac{8}{9} =$ _____

b. _____ $= 1\frac{1}{3} * 2\frac{1}{5}$

c. _____ $= 4\frac{1}{6} * 3\frac{1}{3}$

d. _____ $= \frac{25}{6} * \frac{8}{9}$

e. _____ $= 5 * 2\frac{5}{7}$

SRB
76–78

---

5. The water in Leroy's fish tank had evaporated so that it was about $\frac{5}{8}$ inch below the level it should be. He added water and the water level went up about $\frac{3}{4}$ inch. Did the water level end up above or below where it should be? How much above or below?

Number model: _____

Answer: _____

SRB
66 67
243

---

6. Insert parentheses to make each expression true.

a. $-28 + 43 * 2 = 30$

b. $-19 = 12 / 2 * 6 + (-20)$

c. $16 = 12 / 2 * 6 + (-20)$

d. $24 / 6 - (-2) + 5 = 8$

e. $24 / 6 - (-2) + 5 = 11$

SRB
222

Date

Reference

Place-Value Chart

trillions	100B	10B	billions	100M	10M	millions	hundred-thousands	ten-thousands	thousands	hundreds	tens	ones	.	tenths	hundredths	thousandths
1,000 billions			1,000 millions			1,000,000s	100,000s	10,000s	1,000s	100s	10s	1s	.	0.1s	0.01s	0.001s
10^{12}	10^{11}	10^{10}	10^9	10^8	10^7	10^6	10^5	10^4	10^3	10^2	10^1	10^0	.	10^{-1}	10^{-2}	10^{-3}

Probability Meter

Symbols

+	plus or positive
−	minus or negative
*, ×	multiplied by
÷, /	divided by
=	is equal to
≠	is not equal to
<	is less than
>	is greater than
≤	is less than or equal to
≥	is greater than or equal to
x^n	nth power of x
$\sqrt{x}$	square root of x
%	percent
$\frac{a}{b}$, $a{:}b$, a/b	the fraction $\frac{a}{b}$, ratio of a to b, or a divided by b
°	degree
(a,b)	ordered pair
$\overleftrightarrow{AS}$	line AS
$\overline{AS}$	line segment AS
$\overrightarrow{AS}$	ray AS
∟	right angle
⊥	is perpendicular to
‖	is parallel to
△ABC	triangle ABC
∠ABC	angle ABC
∠B	angle B

Reference

Equivalent Fractions, Decimals, and Percents

															Decimal	Percent
$\frac{1}{2}$	$\frac{2}{4}$	$\frac{3}{6}$	$\frac{4}{8}$	$\frac{5}{10}$	$\frac{6}{12}$	$\frac{7}{14}$	$\frac{8}{16}$	$\frac{9}{18}$	$\frac{10}{20}$	$\frac{11}{22}$	$\frac{12}{24}$	$\frac{13}{26}$	$\frac{14}{28}$	$\frac{15}{30}$	0.5	50%
$\frac{1}{3}$	$\frac{2}{6}$	$\frac{3}{9}$	$\frac{4}{12}$	$\frac{5}{15}$	$\frac{6}{18}$	$\frac{7}{21}$	$\frac{8}{24}$	$\frac{9}{27}$	$\frac{10}{30}$	$\frac{11}{33}$	$\frac{12}{36}$	$\frac{13}{39}$	$\frac{14}{42}$	$\frac{15}{45}$	$0.\overline{3}$	$33\frac{1}{3}\%$
$\frac{2}{3}$	$\frac{4}{6}$	$\frac{6}{9}$	$\frac{8}{12}$	$\frac{10}{15}$	$\frac{12}{18}$	$\frac{14}{21}$	$\frac{16}{24}$	$\frac{18}{27}$	$\frac{20}{30}$	$\frac{22}{33}$	$\frac{24}{36}$	$\frac{26}{39}$	$\frac{28}{42}$	$\frac{30}{45}$	$0.\overline{6}$	$66\frac{2}{3}\%$
$\frac{1}{4}$	$\frac{2}{8}$	$\frac{3}{12}$	$\frac{4}{16}$	$\frac{5}{20}$	$\frac{6}{24}$	$\frac{7}{28}$	$\frac{8}{32}$	$\frac{9}{36}$	$\frac{10}{40}$	$\frac{11}{44}$	$\frac{12}{48}$	$\frac{13}{52}$	$\frac{14}{56}$	$\frac{15}{60}$	0.25	25%
$\frac{3}{4}$	$\frac{6}{8}$	$\frac{9}{12}$	$\frac{12}{16}$	$\frac{15}{20}$	$\frac{18}{24}$	$\frac{21}{28}$	$\frac{24}{32}$	$\frac{27}{36}$	$\frac{30}{40}$	$\frac{33}{44}$	$\frac{36}{48}$	$\frac{39}{52}$	$\frac{42}{56}$	$\frac{45}{60}$	0.75	75%
$\frac{1}{5}$	$\frac{2}{10}$	$\frac{3}{15}$	$\frac{4}{20}$	$\frac{5}{25}$	$\frac{6}{30}$	$\frac{7}{35}$	$\frac{8}{40}$	$\frac{9}{45}$	$\frac{10}{50}$	$\frac{11}{55}$	$\frac{12}{60}$	$\frac{13}{65}$	$\frac{14}{70}$	$\frac{15}{75}$	0.2	20%
$\frac{2}{5}$	$\frac{4}{10}$	$\frac{6}{15}$	$\frac{8}{20}$	$\frac{10}{25}$	$\frac{12}{30}$	$\frac{14}{35}$	$\frac{16}{40}$	$\frac{18}{45}$	$\frac{20}{50}$	$\frac{22}{55}$	$\frac{24}{60}$	$\frac{26}{65}$	$\frac{28}{70}$	$\frac{30}{75}$	0.4	40%
$\frac{3}{5}$	$\frac{6}{10}$	$\frac{9}{15}$	$\frac{12}{20}$	$\frac{15}{25}$	$\frac{18}{30}$	$\frac{21}{35}$	$\frac{24}{40}$	$\frac{27}{45}$	$\frac{30}{50}$	$\frac{33}{55}$	$\frac{36}{60}$	$\frac{39}{65}$	$\frac{42}{70}$	$\frac{45}{75}$	0.6	60%
$\frac{4}{5}$	$\frac{8}{10}$	$\frac{12}{15}$	$\frac{16}{20}$	$\frac{20}{25}$	$\frac{24}{30}$	$\frac{28}{35}$	$\frac{32}{40}$	$\frac{36}{45}$	$\frac{40}{50}$	$\frac{44}{55}$	$\frac{48}{60}$	$\frac{52}{65}$	$\frac{56}{70}$	$\frac{60}{75}$	0.8	80%
$\frac{1}{6}$	$\frac{2}{12}$	$\frac{3}{18}$	$\frac{4}{24}$	$\frac{5}{30}$	$\frac{6}{36}$	$\frac{7}{42}$	$\frac{8}{48}$	$\frac{9}{54}$	$\frac{10}{60}$	$\frac{11}{66}$	$\frac{12}{72}$	$\frac{13}{78}$	$\frac{14}{84}$	$\frac{15}{90}$	$0.1\overline{6}$	$16\frac{2}{3}\%$
$\frac{5}{6}$	$\frac{10}{12}$	$\frac{15}{18}$	$\frac{20}{24}$	$\frac{25}{30}$	$\frac{30}{36}$	$\frac{35}{42}$	$\frac{40}{48}$	$\frac{45}{54}$	$\frac{50}{60}$	$\frac{55}{66}$	$\frac{60}{72}$	$\frac{65}{78}$	$\frac{70}{84}$	$\frac{75}{90}$	$0.8\overline{3}$	$83\frac{1}{3}\%$
$\frac{1}{7}$	$\frac{2}{14}$	$\frac{3}{21}$	$\frac{4}{28}$	$\frac{5}{35}$	$\frac{6}{42}$	$\frac{7}{49}$	$\frac{8}{56}$	$\frac{9}{63}$	$\frac{10}{70}$	$\frac{11}{77}$	$\frac{12}{84}$	$\frac{13}{91}$	$\frac{14}{98}$	$\frac{15}{105}$	0.143	14.3%
$\frac{2}{7}$	$\frac{4}{14}$	$\frac{6}{21}$	$\frac{8}{28}$	$\frac{10}{35}$	$\frac{12}{42}$	$\frac{14}{49}$	$\frac{16}{56}$	$\frac{18}{63}$	$\frac{20}{70}$	$\frac{22}{77}$	$\frac{24}{84}$	$\frac{26}{91}$	$\frac{28}{98}$	$\frac{30}{105}$	0.286	28.6%
$\frac{3}{7}$	$\frac{6}{14}$	$\frac{9}{21}$	$\frac{12}{28}$	$\frac{15}{35}$	$\frac{18}{42}$	$\frac{21}{49}$	$\frac{24}{56}$	$\frac{27}{63}$	$\frac{30}{70}$	$\frac{33}{77}$	$\frac{36}{84}$	$\frac{39}{91}$	$\frac{42}{98}$	$\frac{45}{105}$	0.429	42.9%
$\frac{4}{7}$	$\frac{8}{14}$	$\frac{12}{21}$	$\frac{16}{28}$	$\frac{20}{35}$	$\frac{24}{42}$	$\frac{28}{49}$	$\frac{32}{56}$	$\frac{36}{63}$	$\frac{40}{70}$	$\frac{44}{77}$	$\frac{48}{84}$	$\frac{52}{91}$	$\frac{56}{98}$	$\frac{60}{105}$	0.571	57.1%
$\frac{5}{7}$	$\frac{10}{14}$	$\frac{15}{21}$	$\frac{20}{28}$	$\frac{25}{35}$	$\frac{30}{42}$	$\frac{35}{49}$	$\frac{40}{56}$	$\frac{45}{63}$	$\frac{50}{70}$	$\frac{55}{77}$	$\frac{60}{84}$	$\frac{65}{91}$	$\frac{70}{98}$	$\frac{75}{105}$	0.714	71.4%
$\frac{6}{7}$	$\frac{12}{14}$	$\frac{18}{21}$	$\frac{24}{28}$	$\frac{30}{35}$	$\frac{36}{42}$	$\frac{42}{49}$	$\frac{48}{56}$	$\frac{54}{63}$	$\frac{60}{70}$	$\frac{66}{77}$	$\frac{72}{84}$	$\frac{78}{91}$	$\frac{84}{98}$	$\frac{90}{105}$	0.857	85.7%
$\frac{1}{8}$	$\frac{2}{16}$	$\frac{3}{24}$	$\frac{4}{32}$	$\frac{5}{40}$	$\frac{6}{48}$	$\frac{7}{56}$	$\frac{8}{64}$	$\frac{9}{72}$	$\frac{10}{80}$	$\frac{11}{88}$	$\frac{12}{96}$	$\frac{13}{104}$	$\frac{14}{112}$	$\frac{15}{120}$	0.125	$12\frac{1}{2}\%$
$\frac{3}{8}$	$\frac{6}{16}$	$\frac{9}{24}$	$\frac{12}{32}$	$\frac{15}{40}$	$\frac{18}{48}$	$\frac{21}{56}$	$\frac{24}{64}$	$\frac{27}{72}$	$\frac{30}{80}$	$\frac{33}{88}$	$\frac{36}{96}$	$\frac{39}{104}$	$\frac{42}{112}$	$\frac{45}{120}$	0.375	$37\frac{1}{2}\%$
$\frac{5}{8}$	$\frac{10}{16}$	$\frac{15}{24}$	$\frac{20}{32}$	$\frac{25}{40}$	$\frac{30}{48}$	$\frac{35}{56}$	$\frac{40}{64}$	$\frac{45}{72}$	$\frac{50}{80}$	$\frac{55}{88}$	$\frac{60}{96}$	$\frac{65}{104}$	$\frac{70}{112}$	$\frac{75}{120}$	0.625	$62\frac{1}{2}\%$
$\frac{7}{8}$	$\frac{14}{16}$	$\frac{21}{24}$	$\frac{28}{32}$	$\frac{35}{40}$	$\frac{42}{48}$	$\frac{49}{56}$	$\frac{56}{64}$	$\frac{63}{72}$	$\frac{70}{80}$	$\frac{77}{88}$	$\frac{84}{96}$	$\frac{91}{104}$	$\frac{98}{112}$	$\frac{105}{120}$	0.875	$87\frac{1}{2}\%$
$\frac{1}{9}$	$\frac{2}{18}$	$\frac{3}{27}$	$\frac{4}{36}$	$\frac{5}{45}$	$\frac{6}{54}$	$\frac{7}{63}$	$\frac{8}{72}$	$\frac{9}{81}$	$\frac{10}{90}$	$\frac{11}{99}$	$\frac{12}{108}$	$\frac{13}{117}$	$\frac{14}{126}$	$\frac{15}{135}$	$0.\overline{1}$	$11\frac{1}{9}\%$
$\frac{2}{9}$	$\frac{4}{18}$	$\frac{6}{27}$	$\frac{8}{36}$	$\frac{10}{45}$	$\frac{12}{54}$	$\frac{14}{63}$	$\frac{16}{72}$	$\frac{18}{81}$	$\frac{20}{90}$	$\frac{22}{99}$	$\frac{24}{108}$	$\frac{26}{117}$	$\frac{28}{126}$	$\frac{30}{135}$	$0.\overline{2}$	$22\frac{2}{9}\%$
$\frac{4}{9}$	$\frac{8}{18}$	$\frac{12}{27}$	$\frac{16}{36}$	$\frac{20}{45}$	$\frac{24}{54}$	$\frac{28}{63}$	$\frac{32}{72}$	$\frac{36}{81}$	$\frac{40}{90}$	$\frac{44}{99}$	$\frac{48}{108}$	$\frac{52}{117}$	$\frac{56}{126}$	$\frac{60}{135}$	$0.\overline{4}$	$44\frac{4}{9}\%$
$\frac{5}{9}$	$\frac{10}{18}$	$\frac{15}{27}$	$\frac{20}{36}$	$\frac{25}{45}$	$\frac{30}{54}$	$\frac{35}{63}$	$\frac{40}{72}$	$\frac{45}{81}$	$\frac{50}{90}$	$\frac{55}{99}$	$\frac{60}{108}$	$\frac{65}{117}$	$\frac{70}{126}$	$\frac{75}{135}$	$0.\overline{5}$	$55\frac{5}{9}\%$
$\frac{7}{9}$	$\frac{14}{18}$	$\frac{21}{27}$	$\frac{28}{36}$	$\frac{35}{45}$	$\frac{42}{54}$	$\frac{49}{63}$	$\frac{56}{72}$	$\frac{63}{81}$	$\frac{70}{90}$	$\frac{77}{99}$	$\frac{84}{108}$	$\frac{91}{117}$	$\frac{98}{126}$	$\frac{105}{135}$	$0.\overline{7}$	$77\frac{7}{9}\%$
$\frac{8}{9}$	$\frac{16}{18}$	$\frac{24}{27}$	$\frac{32}{36}$	$\frac{40}{45}$	$\frac{48}{54}$	$\frac{56}{63}$	$\frac{64}{72}$	$\frac{72}{81}$	$\frac{80}{90}$	$\frac{88}{99}$	$\frac{96}{108}$	$\frac{104}{117}$	$\frac{112}{126}$	$\frac{120}{135}$	$0.\overline{8}$	$88\frac{8}{9}\%$

Note: The decimals for sevenths have been rounded to the nearest thousandth.

Reference

The First 100 Prime Numbers

2	3	5	7	11	13	17	19	23	29
31	37	41	43	47	53	59	61	67	71
73	79	83	89	97	101	103	107	109	113
127	131	137	139	149	151	157	163	167	173
179	181	191	193	197	199	211	223	227	229
233	239	241	251	257	263	269	271	277	281
283	293	307	311	313	317	331	337	347	349
353	359	367	373	379	383	389	397	401	409
419	421	431	433	439	443	449	457	461	463
467	479	487	491	499	503	509	521	523	541

Fraction-Stick and Decimal Number-Line Chart

Reference

Metric System

Units of Length

1 kilometer (km)	= 1,000 meters (m)
1 meter	= 10 decimeters (dm)
	= 100 centimeters (cm)
	= 1,000 millimeters (mm)
1 decimeter	= 10 centimeters
1 centimeter	= 10 millimeters

Units of Area

1 square meter (m^2)	= 100 square decimeters (dm^2)
	= 10,000 square centimeters (cm^2)
1 square decimeter	= 100 square centimeters
1 are (a)	= 100 square meters
1 hectare (ha)	= 100 ares
1 square kilometer (km^2)	= 100 hectares

Units of Volume

1 cubic meter (m^3)	= 1,000 cubic decimeters (dm^3)
	= 1,000,000 cubic centimeters (cm^3)
1 cubic decimeter	= 1,000 cubic centimeters

Units of Capacity

1 kiloliter (kL)	= 1,000 liters (L)
1 liter	= 1,000 milliliters (mL)

Units of Mass

1 metric ton (t)	= 1,000 kilograms (kg)
1 kilogram	= 1,000 grams (g)
1 gram	= 1,000 milligrams (mg)

Units of Time

1 century	= 100 years
1 decade	= 10 years
1 year (yr)	= 12 months
	= 52 weeks (plus one or two days)
	= 365 days (366 days in a leap year)
1 month (mo)	= 28, 29, 30, or 31 days
1 week (wk)	= 7 days
1 day (d)	= 24 hours
1 hour (hr)	= 60 minutes
1 minute (min)	= 60 seconds (sec)

U.S. Customary System

Units of Length

1 mile (mi)	= 1,760 yards (yd)
	= 5,280 feet (ft)
1 yard	= 3 feet
	= 36 inches (in.)
1 foot	= 12 inches

Units of Area

1 square yard (yd^2)	= 9 square feet (ft^2)
	= 1,296 square inches (in^2)
1 square foot	= 144 square inches
1 acre	= 43,560 square feet
1 square mile (mi^2)	= 640 acres

Units of Volume

1 cubic yard (yd^3)	= 27 cubic feet (ft^3)
1 cubic foot	= 1,728 cubic inches (in^3)

Units of Capacity

1 gallon (gal)	= 4 quarts (qt)
1 quart	= 2 pints (pt)
1 pint	= 2 cups (c)
1 cup	= 8 fluid ounces (fl oz)
1 fluid ounce	= 2 tablespoons (tbs)
1 tablespoon	= 3 teaspoons (tsp)

Units of Weight

1 ton (T)	= 2,000 pounds (lb)
1 pound	= 16 ounces (oz)

System Equivalents

1 inch is about 2.5 cm (2.54).

1 kilometer is about 0.6 mile (0.621).

1 mile is about 1.6 kilometers (1.609).

1 meter is about 39 inches (39.37).

1 liter is about 1.1 quarts (1.057).

1 ounce is about 28 grams (28.350).

1 kilogram is about 2.2 pounds (2.205).

1 hectare is about 2.5 acres (2.47).

Rules for Order of Operations

1. Do operations within parentheses or other grouping symbols before doing anything else.
2. Calculate all exponents.
3. Multiply or divide, from left to right.
4. Add or subtract, from left to right.

Contents

California Projects

Drawing Geometric Figures

PROJECT 9

Draw and label the following:

1. point *A*	2. $\overleftrightarrow{BC}$
3. $\overline{DE}$	**4.** $\overline{FG} \parallel \overline{HJ}$
5. $\overline{MN} \perp \overline{OP}$	**6.** Line segment *RS* that is perpendicular to parallel lines *WX* and *YZ*
7. acute angle *BDC*	**8.** right angle *HFE*

Date

Constructing Squares

The constructions below are for drawing squares and for using squares to make designs. Follow the directions and draw each construction on a separate sheet of blank paper.

Construction 1: Draw a square

1. Draw a right angle. Label the vertex *A*.

2. With a compass anchor at *A*, draw an arc that intersects the sides of the angle. Label the points of intersection *B* and *C*.

3. Keep the compass opening the same. With the anchor at *B*, draw an arc on the right side of *B*.

4. Keep the compass opening the same. With the anchor at *C*, draw an arc above *C*. The two arcs should now intersect. Label the point of intersection *D*.

5. Draw line segments *BD* and *DC* to form square *ABDC*.

Construction 2: Make a design of squares

1. Draw a square with 4-inch sides. Label the vertices *E, F, G,* and *H*.

2. Use a ruler and mark the middle (midpoints) of each side. Label these points *I, J, K,* and *L*.

3. Draw line segments *IJ, JK, KL,* and *LI* to form square *IJKL*.

4. Draw dotted diagonal line segments *EG* and *FH*. These diagonals intersect the middles of the sides of square *IJKL*.

5. Draw line segments to connect the midpoints of square *IJKL* to form a new square.

6. Continue to form new squares by drawing diagonals, as needed, and connecting midpoints.

7. Use colored pencils or markers to color your design.

Perspective Drawings

When you observe objects over a distance, lines that are parallel will appear to intersect at a distant point. For example, if you look down a road, the sides of the road will appear to be moving closer together. The point where the sides would meet is called the vanishing point. The vanishing point is used in perspective drawings to make 2-dimensional drawings seem more realistic.

In perspective drawings, lines that in reality would be parallel are drawn to intersect at the vanishing point. The more distant an object is to appear, the smaller the object is drawn, but with the same shape and proportions that the object would have if viewed at shorter distances.

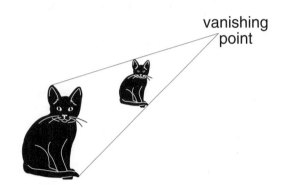

vanishing point

The picture below represents a hallway and shows one window on one wall. Because the picture is in perspective, the window is a trapezoid, not the rectangle it would be in real life.

1. Draw two more windows on the wall. Assume that the three windows are the same size and in the same position from the ceiling and floor.

2. Explain how you can use parallel lines to make sure that you have drawn trapezoids that are similar polygons. Hint: Draw a diagonal in each window.

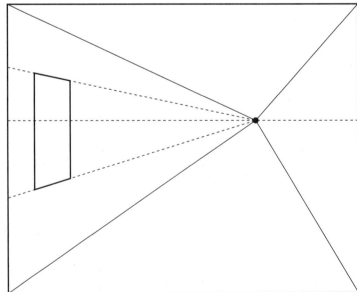

Measurement and Geometry **2.1**

Date _____

Drawing Prisms and Pyramids

One method of drawing a cube is to first draw overlapping squares (with corresponding sides parallel) and then draw lines to connect the vertices. Rectangular, triangular, pentagonal, and hexagonal prisms can be drawn in the same way. Prisms are named for the shape of their bases. Use the Geometry Template or trace pattern blocks to begin. Then overlap the congruent shapes (so that corresponding sides are parallel) and connect the vertices.

1. Draw each of the named prisms below.

Rectangular Prism	Triangular Prism
Hexagonal Prism	**Pentagonal Prism**

Like prisms, pyramids are named for the shape of their bases. All of the faces of a pyramid are triangular and meet at the apex.

The apex is the vertex opposite the base.

2. On a separate piece of paper, follow the steps below to draw a square pyramid.

   Step 1 Draw the base. In this case, the base is a square.

   Step 2 Draw a point on the outside of the base. This is the apex.

   Step 3 Use a straightedge to draw lines to connect each vertex of the base to the apex.

   Step 4 Erase the edges you would not see when looking at a solid pyramid.

Date _____

Drawing Orthographic Views

Isometric drawings represent 3-dimensional objects that have rectangular faces. They show two sides and the top, or the bottom, of the object. An orthographic drawing shows the length, height, and width of the object when you view the object from the top (or bottom), front, and right side. It also shows the parallel edges.

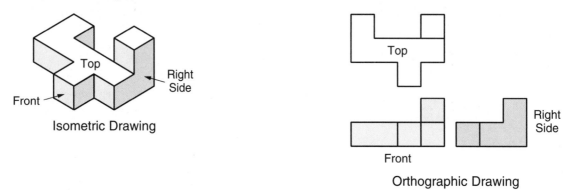

For each isometric drawing below, draw the orthographic views—the top, front, and right sides. You might want to make the objects from centimeter cubes to help you draw the orthographic views. You should show only the parallel edges on each view.

Isometric Drawing	Orthographic Views		
	Top	**Front**	**Right Side**

Measurement and Geometry 2.3

Date _____

There are certain facts that are true of all numbers and that are used to solve mathematical problems. These facts are called properties. When you rewrite a multiplication expression to show the parts of one or more of the factors, you are using the **distributive property:** $a * (b + c) = (a * b) + (a * c)$. For example, when you solve $4 * 76$ with partial products, you think of 76 as $70 + 6$ and multiply each part by 4. The distributive property says: $4 * (70 + 6) = (4 * 70) + (4 * 6)$.

1. Complete the table.

9 * 68 = _____	(9 * 60) + (9 * ____) = _____
____ * ____ = _____	(8 * 70) + (____ * 6) = 608
34 * 97 = _____	(30 * 90) + (30 * 7) + (____ * 90) + (____ * ____) = _____
___ * _____ = _____	(5 * 800) + (____ * 40) + (____ * 7) = _____

2. Cynthia's family wanted to carpet their living room and dining room. The living room measured 9 feet by 12 feet. The dining room measured 9 feet by 9 feet. Use the distributive property to find the total area for the two rooms. Write the number model you used to find your answer.

   Solution: _____
   (unit)

   Number model: _____

   _____

3. Rafael makes picture frames. He gets $12 for each frame. One week Rafael made 19 frames, but the store returned 4 of the frames. Use the distributive property to write an equation to show how much money Rafael will make.

   _____

   _____

4. Use the distributive property to mentally solve the following problems.

   a. 3 * 42 = _____   **b.** 4 * 26 = _____   **c.** 5 * 132 = _____

Date _____

Distributive Property with Variables

You know that with number sentences, the operations inside of parentheses are done first. What happens when you need to multiply expressions in parentheses that contain variables? The distributive property allows you to rewrite the expressions to remove the parentheses. This is called simplifying the expression. For example, $4 * (a + 7) = 4a + 28$.

Complete the problems below by simplifying the expressions.

1. $6 * (a + 8) =$ _____

2. _____ $= 7 * (q + 14)$

3. $3 * (x + y + 27) =$ _____

4. _____ $= (p - 9) * 25$

5. $62 * (6 - j) =$ _____

6. $4 * (n + m) + 9 * (t + u) =$ _____

7. _____ $= 23 * (v + w) + 32 * (e + f)$

8. Marlene was completing a three-day walk to raise money for her local library. She planned to walk the same distance each day. She knew she would walk 7 miles each morning, but she wasn't sure how far she would walk each afternoon. Use a variable to write a number model for the total amount Marlene would walk in 3 days.

   _____

9. Use your number model to find the total amount Marlene walked in Problem 8 if she walked 12 miles each afternoon.

   Solution: _____
                              (unit)

   Number model: _____

10. Niko, Norman, and Nadia were collecting cans to recycle. Each student collected the same number of cans each day. The first week, Niko collected 50 cans per day, Norman collected 100 cans per day, and Nadia collected n cans per day.

    a. Write a number model to show the total cans collected the first week.

       _____

    b. Simplify your number model.

       _____

Algebra and Functions 1.3; Mathematical Reasoning 1.2

Date _____

1. A local newspaper decided to give bonuses to its delivery workers. The paper gave $2,365 in bonuses, which was shared evenly by 6 workers. How much did each worker get?

   _____

2. $837 / 3

   Answer: _____

3. $2,257 / 5

   Answer: _____

4. $8,091 / 9

   Answer: _____

5. 782 / 4

   Answer: _____

PROJECT 12 **Using Long Division** *continued*

6. The fifth graders at Freemont School washed cars to raise money for instruments for their music classes. They worked for two Saturdays and raised $632. If they charged $8 for each car they washed, how many cars did they wash?

_____

7. Write a number story that fits $750 / 8. Then solve your number story.

_____

_____

_____

_____

Solution: _____

Fill in the missing digits in these long division problems.

8.
```
      □ 8 5
   4)7 4 2
   - 4
     ─────
     3 □
   - 3 2
     ─────
       2 2
     - □□
     ─────
         2
```

9.
```
         5 9 2
   □)4 □ 4 5
    - 3 5
      ─────
      6 □
    - □ 3
      ─────
        1 5
      - □□
        ─────
          □
```

Date _____

1. Holmes School had a carnival to raise money for classroom supplies. The carnival raised $6,714, which was to be shared equally by all 27 teachers at Holmes. How much should each teacher have received?

_____

2. $4,864 / 32

   Answer: _____

3. $17,187 / 43

   Answer: _____

4. 5,238 / 27

   Answer: _____

5. 4,785 / 87

   Answer: _____

PROJECT 12

Long Division With Multidigit Divisors *cont.*

6. All 1,237 students at John Muir Elementary School are going on a field trip to the museum. They will take school buses that can each hold 32 students. How many buses will be needed?

_____

7. Write a number story that fits 8,792 / 24. Then solve your number story.

_____

_____

_____

_____

Solution: _____

8. 8,960 / 15

Answer: _____

9. 59,241 / 31

Answer: _____

Long Division Puzzles

Follow these steps to make a long division puzzle:

1. Make up a division problem and use long division to solve it.

2. Check that your answer is correct.

3. Copy your long division work on a separate piece of paper, but leave blanks for some of the digits.

4. Trade your puzzle with a partner. Can you solve your partner's puzzle?

Date _____

Emma's work for a math problem looked like this:

		2	.	8	9
6	$	1 7	.	3	5
	−	1 2			
		5	3		
	−	4	8		
			5	5	
		−	5	4	
				1	

1. What problem was
    Emma trying to solve? _____

2. What answer did Emma get? _____ Was she correct? _____

How do you know? _____

_____

_____

3. Use Emma's method to solve $47.95 / 5. Show your work.

Solve. Show your work on a separate sheet of paper.

4. $142.24 / 8 = _____

5. $28.75 / 25 = _____

6. $5.00 ÷ 3 _____

7. $783 / 4 _____

PROJECT 13

Long Division with Decimal Dividends CALIFORNIA

Use long division to solve these problems. Give your answers to the nearest hundredth.

1. A garden snail travels 7.95 feet in 3 minutes. What is the snail's average speed in feet per minute?

   _____
   (unit)

2. The men's course record for the Davis 12-hour Challenge bicycle race in Winters, California, is held by Andrew Otto, who rode 224 miles in 12 hours. What was Otto's average speed in miles per hour?

   _____
   (unit)

3. The women's course record for the Davis 12-hour Challenge is held by Sandy Earl, who rode 214 miles in 12 hours. What was Earl's average speed in miles per hour?

   _____
   (unit)

Sources: *Encyclopedia Britannica*, www.britannica.com

Davis Bike Club, www.davisbikeclub.org

Number Sense 2.2

Date _____

Read *Student Reference Book*, page 54I with a partner. Then use long division to rename the fractions below as decimals.

1. $\frac{4}{9} =$ _____

2. $\frac{5}{9} =$ _____

3. $\frac{7}{9} =$ _____

4. $\frac{2}{11} =$ _____

5. $\frac{3}{11} =$ _____

6. $\frac{7}{11} =$ _____

7. What pattern do you notice when you rename ninths as decimals?

_____

_____

_____

_____

8. What pattern do you notice when you rename elevenths as decimals?

_____

_____

_____

_____

PROJECT 14 **Dividing with Decimal Divisors**

1. Draw lines to connect each number model with the number story that fits it best.

Number Model	Number Story

2 * 0.10

What is the area of a rectangle 1.75 m by 50 cm?

1.75 * 0.50

Sales tax is 10%. What is the sales tax on a $2 purchase?

2 / 0.10

How many dimes are there in $2?

1.75 / 0.50

A rectangle's area is 8 cm² and its width is 0.25 cm. What is its length?

8 / 0.25

How many 50-cm pieces can be cut from 1.75 m of string?

Find equivalent problems with no decimals in the divisors and solve.

2. 38 / 0.5 = _____
                    equivalent problem

Solution: _____

3. 0.84 / 0.07 = _____
                        equivalent problem

Solution: _____

4. 501 / 0.03 = _____
                       equivalent problem

Solution: _____

5. 0.465 / 1.5 = _____
                        equivalent problem

Solution: _____

6. Indy cars use about 1.3 gallons of fuel for each 2.5-mile lap. How many miles per gallon is that?

_____
                    (unit)

Number Sense **2.2**

PROJECT 14

Representing Remainders as Decimals

You might write the answer to a problem such as 17 / 6 in two ways: 17 / 6 → 2 R 5, or by rewriting the remainder as a fraction: 17 / 6 = $2\frac{5}{6}$.

With decimal long division, you can show the quotient as a decimal: 17 / 6 = $2.8\overline{3}$. The repeat bar means that the 3s repeat forever. But, in most situations, having infinitely many 3s is not practical, so answers are often rounded to some reasonable number of decimal places, usually two or three: 17 / 6 = 2.83, or 17 / 6 = 2.833.

Notice that 17 / 6 = 2.83 is not actually true. You can check this by multiplying 2.83 by 6. You won't get 17. But, for most practical purposes, 2.83 or 2.833 is close enough to 17 / 6 that most people aren't bothered by a rounded number model.

Complete the table.

Problem	Answer as			
	Quotient and Remainder	Mixed Number	Exact Decimal	Decimal Rounded to Hundredths
1. 17 / 6	2 R5	$2\frac{5}{6}$	$2.8\overline{3}$	2.83
2. 15 / 4				
3. 5 / 8				
4. 17 / 3				
5. 56 / 9				

Date _____

Division by Unit Fractions

Division can be used to find how many _____ are in _____. For example, you can answer, "How many 8s are in 168?" by solving 168 / 8. You can answer, "How many quarters are in $3?" by solving $3 \div \frac{1}{4}$.

Drawing "hops" on a number line can help you solve some division problems. Draw hops on the number lines to help you solve Problems 1–4.

Example:

$1 \div \frac{1}{5} = 5$

1. $1 \div \frac{1}{4} =$ _____

2. $1 \div \frac{1}{3} =$ _____

3. $2 \div \frac{1}{2} =$ _____

4. $2\frac{2}{3} \div \frac{1}{3} =$ _____

5. $22 \div \frac{1}{2} =$ _____

6. $14 \div \frac{1}{5} =$ _____

7. What pattern do you notice when you divide by a unit fraction? (A unit fraction is a fraction with a numerator of 1; $\frac{1}{2}$, $\frac{1}{3}$, $\frac{1}{4}$, and so on are unit fractions.)

_____

_____

_____

8. Write a rule for dividing by a unit fraction.

_____

Date _____

Dividing by a fraction is the same as first dividing by the unit fraction with the same denominator and then dividing by the numerator.

Example:

$$\frac{3}{2} \div \frac{3}{4} = \left(\frac{3}{2} \div \frac{1}{4}\right) \div 3$$

$$= \left(\frac{3}{2} * 4\right) \div 3 \text{ Dividing by } \frac{1}{4} \text{ is the same as multiplying by 4.}$$

$$= \left(\frac{3}{2} * 4\right) * \frac{1}{3} \text{ Dividing by 3 is the same as multiplying by } \frac{1}{3}.$$

$$= \left(\frac{3}{2} * \frac{4}{3}\right) = \frac{3 * 4}{2 * 3} = \frac{12}{6} = 2$$

Jumping by $\frac{3}{4}$s on a number line also shows that $\frac{3}{2} \div \frac{3}{4} = 2$:

Number lines can help with simple fraction division problems, but they're not as useful for harder problems. A way to divide fractions that works for all problems is the invert-and-multiply method, which is similar to the example above. To "invert" means to turn upside down. With fractions, it means to switch the numerator and the denominator. The fraction with numerator and denominator switched is called the **reciprocal** of the fraction you started with. To divide by a fraction using this method, invert that fraction and multiply:

$$\frac{a}{b} \div \frac{c}{d} = \frac{a}{b} * \frac{d}{c}$$

Use the invert-and-multiply method to solve these problems. Put your answers in simplest form.

1. $\frac{2}{5} \div \frac{2}{15}$ _____

2. $\frac{9}{4} \div \frac{3}{8}$ _____

3. $4 \div \frac{1}{2}$ _____

4. $6 \div \frac{2}{3}$ _____

5. $6\frac{1}{2} \div \frac{1}{2}$ _____

6. $7\frac{1}{2} \div \frac{3}{4}$ _____

PROJECT 15 **The Invert-and-Multiply Method** *cont.*

7. A recipe for a raisin cake calls for $\frac{1}{2}$ cup of raisins. How many cakes can you make if you have $2\frac{1}{2}$ cups of raisins?

_____

Write a division number model for this problem.

_____

8. Lisa wants to make hair ties. She needs $1\frac{1}{2}$ feet of ribbon for each tie. If she has $10\frac{1}{2}$ feet of ribbon, then how many hair ties can she make?

_____

Write a division number model for this problem.

_____

9. Write a fraction division number story. Then solve your number story and write a division number model for it.

_____

_____

Solution: _____

Number model: _____

Use the invert-and-multiply method to solve these problems. Put your answers in simplest form.

10. $\frac{1}{3} \div \frac{1}{4}$ _____

11. $\frac{1}{3} \div \frac{1}{2}$ _____

12. $1\frac{3}{8} \div \frac{5}{6}$ _____

13. $\frac{2}{5} \div \frac{2}{3}$ _____

14. $2\frac{1}{2} \div 3\frac{1}{2}$ _____

15. $\frac{1}{4} \div \frac{3}{4}$ _____

Number Sense 2.4; Number Sense 2.5

PROJECT 15 — The Invert-and-Multiply Method *cont.*

16. $\frac{9}{2} \div 2\frac{3}{8}$ _____

17. $15 \div \frac{3}{8}$ _____

18. $1\frac{1}{4} \div 2\frac{1}{8}$ _____

19. $\frac{24}{37} \div \frac{8}{37}$ _____

20. $\frac{1}{2} \div 3\frac{1}{2}$ _____

21. $1\frac{1}{8} \div 2\frac{2}{3}$ _____

Another Way to Divide Fractions

Arjun solved $\frac{3}{10} \div \frac{1}{5}$ by dividing the numerator by the numerator and the denominator by the denominator. This is what he did:

$$\frac{3}{10} \div \frac{1}{5} = \frac{3 \div 1}{10 \div 5}$$

$$= \frac{3}{2}$$

$$= 1\frac{1}{2}$$

Solve some fraction division problems with Arjun's method and also with the invert-and-multiply method or the common-denominator method. Show samples of your work on a separate sheet of paper.

Do you think Arjun's method will always work? _____

_____

_____

Does adding numerators and denominators work in fraction addition? _____

Does multiplying numerators and denominators work for fraction multiplication? _____

California Content Standards

The California Mathematics Content Standards describe what every student in California can and needs to learn in mathematics. These standards are identified at the bottom of each of your journal pages and are listed here for your reference. The oval identifies the key standards for this grade level.

Pages 209, 210

Number Sense 1.3 Understand and compute positive integer powers of nonnegative integers; compute examples as repeated multiplication.

Mathematical Reasoning 2.4 Express the solution clearly and logically by using the appropriate mathematical notation and terms and clear language; support solutions with evidence in both verbal and symbolic work.

Page 212

Number Sense 1.0 Students compute with very large and very small numbers, positive integers, decimals, and fractions and understand the relationship between decimals, fractions, and percents. They understand the relative magnitudes of numbers.

Number Sense 1.1 Estimate, round, and manipulate very large (e.g., millions) and very small (e.g., thousandths) numbers.

Number Sense 1.3 Understand and compute positive integer powers of nonnegative integers; compute examples as repeated multiplication.

Page 214

Number Sense 1.1 Estimate, round, and manipulate very large (e.g., millions) and very small (e.g., thousandths) numbers.

Number Sense 1.3 Understand and compute positive integer powers of nonnegative integers; compute examples as repeated multiplication.

Pages 215, 216

Number Sense 1.1 Estimate, round, and manipulate very large (e.g., millions) and very small (e.g., thousandths) numbers.

Number Sense 1.3 Understand and compute positive integer powers of nonnegative integers; compute examples as repeated multiplication.

Page 217

Number Sense 1.1 Estimate, round, and manipulate very large (e.g., millions) and very small (e.g., thousandths) numbers.

Mathematical Reasoning 1.2 Determine when and how to break a problem into simpler parts.

Pages 219, 220

Mathematical Reasoning 1.1 Analyze problems by identifying relationships, distinguishing relevant from irrelevant information, sequencing and prioritizing information, and observing patterns.

Page 222

Mathematical Reasoning 1.1 Analyze problems by identifying relationships, distinguishing relevant from irrelevant information, sequencing and prioritizing information, and observing patterns.

Page 223

Mathematical Reasoning 1.1 Analyze problems by identifying relationships, distinguishing relevant from irrelevant information, sequencing and prioritizing information, and observing patterns.

Page 224

Number Sense 1.0 Students compute with very large and very small numbers, positive integers, decimals, and fractions and understand the relationship between decimals, fractions, and percents. They understand the relative magnitudes of numbers.

Page 226

Statistics, Data Analysis, and Probability 1.0 Students display, analyze, compare, and interpret different data sets, including data sets of different sizes.

Statistics, Data Analysis, and Probability 1.2 Organize and display single-variable data in appropriate graphs and representations (e.g., histogram, circle graphs) and explain which types of graphs are appropriate for various data sets.

Page 227

Statistics, Data Analysis, and Probability 1.0 Students display, analyze, compare, and interpret different data sets, including data sets of different sizes.

Statistics, Data Analysis, and Probability 1.2 Organize and display single-variable data in appropriate graphs and representations (e.g., histogram, circle graphs) and explain which types of graphs are appropriate for various data sets.

Page 229

Number Sense 1.5 Identify and represent on a number line decimals, fractions, mixed numbers, and positive and negative integers.

Page 230

Number Sense 1.5 Identify and represent on a number line decimals, fractions, mixed numbers, and positive and negative integers.

Page 232

Number Sense 2.1 Add, subtract, multiply, and divide with decimals; add with negative integers; subtract positive integers from negative integers; and verify the reasonableness of the results.

Number Sense 2.2 Add, subtract, multiply, and divide with decimals; add with negative integers; subtract positive integers from negative integers; and verify the reasonableness of the results.

Mathematical Reasoning 2.3 Use a variety of methods, such as words, numbers, symbols, charts, graphs, tables, diagrams, and models, to explain mathematical reasoning.

Page 233

Number Sense 2.1 Add, subtract, multiply, and divide with decimals; add with negative integers; subtract positive integers from negative integers; and verify the reasonableness of the results.

Number Sense 2.2 Add, subtract, multiply, and divide with decimals; add with negative integers; subtract positive integers from negative integers; and verify the reasonableness of the results.

Mathematical Reasoning 2.3 Use a variety of methods, such as words, numbers, symbols, charts, graphs, tables, diagrams, and models, to explain mathematical reasoning.

Page 234

Number Sense 2.1 Add, subtract, multiply, and divide with decimals; add with negative integers; subtract positive integers from negative integers; and verify the reasonableness of the results.

Algebra and Functions 1.0 Students use variables in simple expressions, compute the value of the expressions for specific values of the variable, and plot and interpret the results.

Page 235

Number Sense 2.1 Add, subtract, multiply, and divide with decimals; add with negative integers; subtract positive integers from negative integers; and verify the reasonableness of the results.

Number Sense 2.2 Add, subtract, multiply, and divide with decimals; add with negative integers; subtract positive integers from negative integers; and verify the reasonableness of the results.

Page 237

Number Sense 2.1 Add, subtract, multiply, and divide with decimals; add with negative integers; subtract positive integers from negative integers; and verify the reasonableness of the results.

Number Sense 2.2 Add, subtract, multiply, and divide with decimals; add with negative integers; subtract positive integers from negative integers; and verify the reasonableness of the results.

Mathematical Reasoning 2.3 Use a variety of methods, such as words, numbers, symbols, charts, graphs, tables, diagrams, and models, to explain mathematical reasoning.

Pages 238, 239

Number Sense 2.1 Add, subtract, multiply, and divide with decimals; add with negative integers; subtract positive integers from negative integers; and verify the reasonableness of the results.

Number Sense 2.2 Add, subtract, multiply, and divide with decimals; add with negative integers; subtract positive integers from negative integers; and verify the reasonableness of the results.

Mathematical Reasoning 2.3 Use a variety of methods, such as words, numbers, symbols, charts, graphs, tables, diagrams, and models, to explain mathematical reasoning.

Page 240

Number Sense 2.1 Add, subtract, multiply, and divide with decimals; add with negative integers; subtract positive integers from negative integers; and verify the reasonableness of the results.

Number Sense 2.2 Add, subtract, multiply, and divide with decimals; add with negative integers; subtract positive integers from negative integers; and verify the reasonableness of the results.

Page 242

Number Sense 1.5 Identify and represent on a number line decimals, fractions, mixed numbers, and positive and negative integers.

Number Sense 2.1 Add, subtract, multiply, and divide with decimals; add with negative integers; subtract positive integers from negative integers; and verify the reasonableness of the results.

Number Sense 2.2 Add, subtract, multiply, and divide with decimals; add with negative integers; subtract positive integers from negative integers; and verify the reasonableness of the results.

Pages 244, 245

Number Sense 2.1 Add, subtract, multiply, and divide with decimals; add with negative integers; subtract positive integers from negative integers; and verify the reasonableness of the results.

Number Sense 2.2 Add, subtract, multiply, and divide with decimals; add with negative integers; subtract positive integers from negative integers; and verify the reasonableness of the results.

Page 248

Number Sense 1.0 Students compute with very large and very small numbers, positive integers, decimals, and fractions and understand the relationship between decimals, fractions, and percents. They understand the relative magnitudes of numbers.

Number Sense 1.5 Identify and represent on a number line decimals, fractions, mixed numbers, and positive and negative integers.

Page 249

Number Sense 1.5 Identify and represent on a number line decimals, fractions, mixed numbers, and positive and negative integers.

Number Sense 2.0 Students perform calculations and solve problems involving addition, subtraction, and simple multiplication and division of fractions and decimals.

Number Sense 2.3 Solve simple problems, including ones arising in concrete situations, involving the addition and subtraction of fractions and mixed numbers (like and unlike denominators of 20 or less), and express answers in the simplest form.

Pages 251, 252

Number Sense 2.0 Students perform calculations and solve problems involving addition, subtraction, and simple multiplication and division of fractions and decimals.

Number Sense 2.3 Solve simple problems, including ones arising in concrete situations, involving the addition and subtraction of fractions and mixed numbers (like and unlike denominators of 20 or less), and express answers in the simplest form.

Page 254

Number Sense 2.0 Students perform calculations and solve problems involving addition, subtraction, and simple multiplication and division of fractions and decimals.

Number Sense 2.3 Solve simple problems, including ones arising in concrete situations, involving the addition and subtraction of fractions and mixed numbers (like and unlike denominators of 20 or less), and express answers in the simplest form.

Page 255

Number Sense 2.0 Students perform calculations and solve problems involving addition, subtraction, and simple multiplication and division of fractions and decimals.

Number Sense 2.3 Solve simple problems, including ones arising in concrete situations, involving the addition and subtraction of fractions and mixed numbers (like and unlike denominators of 20 or less), and express answers in the simplest form.

Page 257

Number Sense 2.0 Students perform calculations and solve problems involving addition, subtraction, and simple multiplication and division of fractions and decimals.

Number Sense 2.3 Solve simple problems, including ones arising in concrete situations, involving the addition and subtraction of fractions and mixed numbers (like and unlike denominators of 20 or less), and express answers in the simplest form.

Page 259

Number Sense 1.5 Identify and represent on a number line decimals, fractions, mixed numbers, and positive and negative integers.

Number Sense 2.4 Understand the concept of multiplication and division of fractions.

Number Sense 2.5 Compute and perform simple multiplication and division of fractions and apply these procedures to solving problems.

Pages 260, 261

Number Sense 2.4 Understand the concept of multiplication and division of fractions.

Number Sense 2.5 Compute and perform simple multiplication and division of fractions and apply these procedures to solving problems.

Page 262

Number Sense 2.0 Students perform calculations and solve problems involving addition, subtraction, and simple multiplication and division of fractions and decimals.

Page 264

Number Sense 2.4 Understand the concept of multiplication and division of fractions.

Number Sense 2.5 Compute and perform simple multiplication and division of fractions and apply these procedures to solving problems.

Page 265

Number Sense 2.4 Understand the concept of multiplication and division of fractions.

Number Sense 2.5 Compute and perform simple multiplication and division of fractions and apply these procedures to solving problems.

Mathematical Reasoning 2.3 Use a variety of methods, such as words, numbers, symbols, charts, graphs, tables, diagrams, and models, to explain mathematical reasoning.

Page 266

Number Sense 2.4 Understand the concept of multiplication and division of fractions.

Number Sense 2.5 Compute and perform simple multiplication and division of fractions and apply these procedures to solving problems.

Page 268

Number Sense 1.0 Students compute with very large and very small numbers, positive integers, decimals, and fractions and understand the relationship between decimals, fractions, and percents. They understand the relative magnitudes of numbers.

Number Sense 2.0 Students perform calculations and solve problems involving addition, subtraction, and simple multiplication and division of fractions and decimals.

Number Sense 2.4 Understand the concept of multiplication and division of fractions.

Number Sense 2.5 Compute and perform simple multiplication and division of fractions and apply these procedures to solving problems.

Mathematical Reasoning 2.3 Use a variety of methods, such as words, numbers, symbols, charts, graphs, tables, diagrams, and models, to explain mathematical reasoning.

Page 269

Number Sense 2.4 Understand the concept of multiplication and division of fractions.

Number Sense 2.5 Compute and perform simple multiplication and division of fractions and apply these procedures to solving problems.

Page 270

Number Sense 2.4 Understand the concept of multiplication and division of fractions.

Number Sense 2.5 Compute and perform simple multiplication and division of fractions and apply these procedures to solving problems.

Algebra and Functions 1.0 Students use variables in simple expressions, compute the value of the expressions for specific values of the variable, and plot and interpret the results.

Page 272

Number Sense 1.0 Students compute with very large and very small numbers, positive integers, decimals, and fractions and understand the relationship between decimals, fractions, and percents. They understand the relative magnitudes of numbers.

Number Sense 2.3 Solve simple problems, including ones arising in concrete situations, involving the addition and subtraction of fractions and mixed numbers (like and unlike denominators of 20 or less), and express answers in the simplest form.

Page 273

Number Sense 2.4 Understand the concept of multiplication and division of fractions.

Number Sense 2.5 Compute and perform simple multiplication and division of fractions and apply these procedures to solving problems.

Page 274

Number Sense 2.4 Understand the concept of multiplication and division of fractions.

Number Sense 2.5 Compute and perform simple multiplication and division of fractions and apply these procedures to solving problems.

Page 275

Number Sense 2.5 Compute and perform simple multiplication and division of fractions and apply these procedures to solving problems.

Page 277

Number Sense 1.2 Interpret percents as part of a hundred; find decimal and percent equivalents for common fractions and explain why they represent the same value; compute a given percent of a whole number.

Number Sense 2.4 Understand the concept of multiplication and division of fractions.

Page 278

Number Sense 1.2 Interpret percents as part of a hundred; find decimal and percent equivalents for common fractions and explain why they represent the same value; compute a given percent of a whole number.

Mathematical Reasoning 2.0 Students use strategies, skills, and concepts in finding solutions.

Page 280

Number Sense 1.2 Interpret percents as part of a hundred; find decimal and percent equivalents for common fractions and explain why they represent the same value; compute a given percent of a whole number.

Number Sense 2.4 Understand the concept of multiplication and division of fractions.

Number Sense 2.5 Compute and perform simple multiplication and division of fractions and apply these procedures to solving problems.

Algebra and Functions 1.2 Use a letter to represent an unknown number; write and evaluate simple algebraic expressions in one variable by substitution.

Pages 281, 282

Number Sense 1.2 Interpret percents as part of a hundred; find decimal and percent equivalents for common fractions and explain why they represent the same value; compute a given percent of a whole number.

Number Sense 2.5 Compute and perform simple multiplication and division of fractions and apply these procedures to solving problems.

Algebra and Functions 1.0 Students use variables in simple expressions, compute the value of the expressions for specific values of the variable, and plot and interpret the results.

Mathematical Reasoning 2.0 Students use strategies, skills, and concepts in finding solutions.

Page 284

Number Sense 1.2 Interpret percents as part of a hundred; find decimal and percent equivalents for common fractions and explain why they represent the same value; compute a given percent of a whole number.

Statistics, Data Analysis, and Probability 1.3 Use fractions and percentages to compare data sets of different sizes.

Pages 285, 286

Number Sense 1.1 Estimate, round, and manipulate very large (e.g., millions) and very small (e.g., thousandths) numbers.

Mathematical Reasoning 2.1 Use estimation to verify the reasonableness of calculated results.

Pages 288, 289

Number Sense 2.4 Understand the concept of multiplication and division of fractions.

Number Sense 2.5 Compute and perform simple multiplication and division of fractions and apply these procedures to solving problems.

Page 292

Algebra and Functions 1.4 Identify and graph ordered pairs in the four quadrants of the coordinate plane.

Statistics, Data Analysis, and Probability 1.5 Know how to write ordered pairs correctly; for example, (x, y).

Page 293

Statistics, Data Analysis, and Probability 1.5 Know how to write ordered pairs correctly; for example, (x, y).

CA24

Page 294

Algebra and Functions 1.5 Solve problems involving linear functions with integer values; write the equation; and graph the resulting ordered pairs of integers on a grid.

Statistics, Data Analysis, and Probability 1.4 Identify ordered pairs of data from a graph and interpret the meaning of the data in terms of the situation depicted by the graph.

Pages 296–298

Algebra and Functions 1.4 Identify and graph ordered pairs in the four quadrants of the coordinate plane.

Statistics, Data Analysis, and Probability 1.5 Know how to write ordered pairs correctly; for example, (x, y).

Pages 300, 301

Algebra and Functions 1.4 Identify and graph ordered pairs in the four quadrants of the coordinate plane.

Statistics, Data Analysis, and Probability 1.5 Know how to write ordered pairs correctly; for example, (x, y).

Page 302

Algebra and Functions 1.4 Identify and graph ordered pairs in the four quadrants of the coordinate plane.

Statistics, Data Analysis, and Probability 1.5 Know how to write ordered pairs correctly; for example, (x, y).

Page 304

Measurement and Geometry 1.0 Students understand and compute the volumes and areas of simple objects.

Measurement and Geometry 1.1 Derive and use the formula for the area of a triangle and of a parallelogram by comparing it with the formula for the area of a rectangle (i.e., two of the same triangles make a parallelogram with twice the area; a parallelogram is compared with a rectangle of the same area by cutting and pasting a right triangle on the parallelogram).

Measurement and Geometry 1.4 Differentiate between, and use appropriate units of measures for, two- and three-dimensional objects (i.e., find the perimeter, area, volume).

Page 305

Measurement and Geometry 1.0 Students understand and compute the volumes and areas of simple objects.

Measurement and Geometry 1.1 Derive and use the formula for the area of a triangle and of a parallelogram by comparing it with the formula for the area of a rectangle (i.e., two of the same triangles make a parallelogram with twice the area; a parallelogram is compared with a rectangle of the same area by cutting and pasting a right triangle on the parallelogram).

Measurement and Geometry 1.4 Differentiate between, and use appropriate units of measures for, two- and three-dimensional objects (i.e., find the perimeter, area, volume).

Page 306

Measurement and Geometry 2.0 Students identify, describe, and classify the properties of, and the relationships between, plane and solid geometric figures.

Measurement and Geometry 2.3 Visualize and draw two-dimensional views of three-dimensional objects made from rectangular solids.

Page 308

Measurement and Geometry 1.1 Derive and use the formula for the area of a triangle and of a parallelogram by comparing it with the formula for the area of a rectangle (i.e., two of the same triangles make a parallelogram with twice the area; a parallelogram is compared with a rectangle of the same area by cutting and pasting a right triangle on the parallelogram).

Measurement and Geometry 1.4 Differentiate between, and use appropriate units of measures for, two- and three-dimensional objects (i.e., find the perimeter, area, volume).

Mathematical Reasoning 2.3 Use a variety of methods, such as words, numbers, symbols, charts, graphs, tables, diagrams, and models, to explain mathematical reasoning.

Mathematical Reasoning 3.0 Students move beyond a particular problem by generalizing to other situations.

Page 309

Measurement and Geometry 1.0 Students understand and compute the volumes and areas of simple objects.

Measurement and Geometry 1.1 Derive and use the formula for the area of a triangle and of a parallelogram by comparing it with the formula for the area of a rectangle (i.e., two of the same triangles make a parallelogram with twice the area; a parallelogram is compared with a rectangle of the same area by cutting and pasting a right triangle on the parallelogram).

Measurement and Geometry 1.4 Differentiate between, and use appropriate units of measures for, two- and three-dimensional objects (i.e., find the perimeter, area, volume).

Mathematical Reasoning 3.0 Students move beyond a particular problem by generalizing to other situations.

Page 310

Measurement and Geometry 1.0 Students understand and compute the volumes and areas of simple objects.

Measurement and Geometry 1.1 Derive and use the formula for the area of a triangle and of a parallelogram by comparing it with the formula for the area of a rectangle (i.e., two of the same triangles make a parallelogram with twice the area; a parallelogram is compared with a rectangle of the same area by cutting and pasting a right triangle on the parallelogram).

Measurement and Geometry 1.4 Differentiate between, and use appropriate units of measures for, two- and three-dimensional objects (i.e., find the perimeter, area, volume).

Mathematical Reasoning 3.0 Students move beyond a particular problem by generalizing to other situations.

Mathematical Reasoning 3.2 Note the method of deriving the solution and demonstrate a conceptual understanding of the derivation by solving similar problems.

Page 312

Measurement and Geometry 1.0 Students understand and compute the volumes and areas of simple objects.

Measurement and Geometry 1.1 Derive and use the formula for the area of a triangle and of a parallelogram by comparing it with the formula for the area of a rectangle (i.e., two of the same triangles make a parallelogram with twice the area; a parallelogram is compared with a rectangle of the same area by cutting and pasting a right triangle on the parallelogram).

Measurement and Geometry 1.4 Differentiate between, and use appropriate units of measures for, two- and three-dimensional objects (i.e., find the perimeter, area, volume).

Measurement and Geometry 2.0 Students identify, describe, and classify the properties of, and the relationships between, plane and solid geometric figures.

Page 313

Measurement and Geometry 1.0 Students understand and compute the volumes and areas of simple objects.

Measurement and Geometry 1.1 Derive and use the formula for the area of a triangle and of a parallelogram by comparing each with the formula for the area of a rectangle (i.e., two of the same triangles make a parallelogram with twice the area; a parallelogram is compared with a rectangle of the same area by cutting and pasting a right triangle on the parallelogram).

Measurement and Geometry 1.4 Differentiate between, and use appropriate units of measures for, two- and three-dimensional objects (i.e., find the perimeter, area, volume).

Mathematical Reasoning 3.2 Note the method of deriving the solution and demonstrate a conceptual understanding of the derivation by solving similar problems.

Page 314

Measurement and Geometry 1.0 Students understand and compute the volumes and areas of simple objects.

Measurement and Geometry 1.1 Derive and use the formula for the area of a triangle and of a parallelogram by comparing each with the formula for the area of a rectangle (i.e., two of the same triangles make a parallelogram with twice the area; a parallelogram is compared with a rectangle of the same area by cutting and pasting a right triangle on the parallelogram).

Measurement and Geometry 1.4 Differentiate between, and use appropriate units of measures for, two- and three-dimensional objects (i.e., find the perimeter, area, volume).

Mathematical Reasoning 3.2 Note the method of deriving the solution and demonstrate a conceptual understanding of the derivation by solving similar problems.

Page 316

Mathematical Reasoning 2.1 Use estimation to verify the reasonableness of calculated results.

Pages 317–319

Number Sense 1.1 Estimate, round, and manipulate very large (e.g., millions) and very small (e.g., thousandths) numbers.

Mathematical Reasoning 2.0 Students use strategies, skills, and concepts in finding solutions.

Page 321

Measurement and Geometry 1.2 Construct a cube and rectangular box from two-dimensional patterns and use these patterns to compute the surface area for these objects.

Measurement and Geometry 1.3 Understand the concept of volume and use the appropriate units in common measuring systems (i.e., cubic centimeter [cm^3], cubic meter [m^3], cubic inch [$in.^3$], cubic yard [$yd.^3$]) to compute the volume of rectangular solids.

Measurement and Geometry 1.4 Differentiate between, and use appropriate units of measures for, two- and three-dimensional objects (i.e., find the perimeter, area, volume).

Measurement and Geometry 2.0 Students identify, describe, and classify the properties of, and the relationships between, plane and solid geometric figures.

Page 322

Measurement and Geometry 1.2 Construct a cube and rectangular box from two-dimensional patterns and use these patterns to compute the surface area for these objects.

Measurement and Geometry 1.3 Understand the concept of volume and use the appropriate units in common measuring systems (i.e., cubic centimeter [cm^3], cubic meter [m^3], cubic inch [$in.^3$], cubic yard [$yd.^3$]) to compute the volume of rectangular solids.

Measurement and Geometry 1.4 Differentiate between, and use appropriate units of measures for, two- and three-dimensional objects (i.e., find the perimeter, area, volume).

Pages 324, 325

Measurement and Geometry 1.0 Students understand and compute the volumes and areas of simple objects.

Measurement and Geometry 1.3 Understand the concept of volume and use the appropriate units in common measuring systems (i.e., cubic centimeter [cm^3], cubic meter [m^3], cubic inch [$in.^3$], cubic yard [$yd.^3$]) to compute the volume of rectangular solids.

Measurement and Geometry 1.4 Differentiate between, and use appropriate units of measures for, two- and three-dimensional objects (i.e., find the perimeter, area, volume).

Pages 327, 328

Measurement and Geometry 1.3 Understand the concept of volume and use the appropriate units in common measuring systems (i.e., cubic centimeter [cm^3], cubic meter [m^3], cubic inch [$in.^3$], cubic yard [$yd.^3$]) to compute the volume of rectangular solids.

Measurement and Geometry 1.4 Differentiate between, and use appropriate units of measures for, two- and three-dimensional objects (i.e., find the perimeter, area, volume).

Page 329

Measurement and Geometry 1.2 Construct a cube and rectangular box from two-dimensional patterns and use these patterns to compute the surface area for these objects.

Measurement and Geometry 1.3 Understand the concept of volume and use the appropriate units in common measuring systems (i.e., cubic centimeter [cm^3], cubic meter [m^3], cubic inch [$in.^3$], cubic yard [$yd.^3$]) to compute the volume of rectangular solids.

Measurement and Geometry 1.4 Differentiate between, and use appropriate units of measures for, two- and three-dimensional objects (i.e., find the perimeter, area, volume).

Page 330

Measurement and Geometry 1.0 Students understand and compute the volumes and areas of simple objects.

Measurement and Geometry 1.1 Derive and use the formula for the area of a triangle and of a parallelogram by comparing each with the formula for the area of a rectangle (i.e., two of the same triangles make a parallelogram with twice the area; a parallelogram is compared with a rectangle of the same area by cutting and pasting a right triangle on the parallelogram).

Pages 333, 334

Algebra and Functions 1.0 Students use variables in simple expressions, compute the value of the expression for specific values of the variable, and plot and interpret the results.

Algebra and Functions 1.1 Use information taken from a graph or equation to answer questions about a problem situation.

Mathematical Reasoning 2.3 Use a variety of methods, such as words, numbers, symbols, charts, graphs, tables, diagrams, and models, to explain mathematical reasoning.

Pages 336, 337

Algebra and Functions 1.0 Students use variables in simple expressions, compute the value of the expression for specific values of the variable, and plot and interpret the results.

Algebra and Functions 1.1 Use information taken from a graph or equation to answer questions about a problem situation.

Mathematical Reasoning 1.0 Students make decisions about how to approach problems.

Page 338

Algebra and Functions 1.0 Students use variables in simple expressions, compute the value of the expression for specific values of the variable, and plot and interpret the results.

Algebra and Functions 1.1 Use information taken from a graph or equation to answer questions about a problem situation.

Mathematical Reasoning 1.0 Students make decisions about how to approach problems.

Mathematical Reasoning 2.2 Apply strategies and results from simpler problems to more complex problems.

Mathematical Reasoning 2.3 Use a variety of methods, such as words, numbers, symbols, charts, graphs, tables, diagrams, and models, to explain mathematical reasoning.

Page 339

Algebra and Functions 1.1 Use information taken from a graph or equation to answer questions about a problem situation.

Statistics, Data Analysis, and Probability 1.0 Students display, analyze, compare, and interpret different data sets, including data sets of different sizes.

Statistics, Data Analysis, and Probability 1.2 Organize and display single-variable data in appropriate graphs and representations (e.g., histogram, circle graphs) and explain which types of graphs are appropriate for various data sets.

Statistics, Data Analysis, and Probability 1.4 Identify ordered pairs of data from a graph and interpret the meaning of the data in terms of the situation depicted by the graph.

Pages 341, 342

Algebra and Functions 1.2 Use a letter to represent an unknown number; write and evaluate simple algebraic expressions in one variable by substitution.

Page 343

Algebra and Functions 1.2 Use a letter to represent an unknown number; write and evaluate simple algebraic expressions in one variable by substitution.

Algebra and Functions 1.5 Solve problems involving linear functions with integer values; write the equation; and graph the resulting ordered pairs of integers on a grid.

Pages 346, 347

Algebra and Functions 1.0 Students use variables in simple expressions, compute the value of the expression for specific values of the variable, and plot and interpret the results.

Algebra and Functions 1.1 Use information taken from a graph or equation to answer questions about a problem situation.

Algebra and Functions 1.2 Use a letter to represent an unknown number; write and evaluate simple algebraic expressions in one variable by substitution.

Algebra and Functions 1.5 Solve problems involving linear functions with integer values; write the equation; and graph the resulting ordered pairs of integers on a grid.

Statistics, Data Analysis, and Probability 1.1 Know the concepts of mean, median, and mode; compute and compare simple examples to show that they may differ.

Statistics, Data Analysis, and Probability 1.4 Identify ordered pairs of data from a graph and interpret the meaning of the data in terms of the situation depicted by the graph.

Pages 348, 349

Algebra and Functions 1.0 Students use variables in simple expressions, compute the value of the expression for specific values of the variable, and plot and interpret the results.

Algebra and Functions 1.2 Use a letter to represent an unknown number; write and evaluate simple algebraic expressions in one variable by substitution.

Algebra and Functions 1.5 Solve problems involving linear functions with integer values; write the equation; and graph the resulting ordered pairs of integers on a grid.

Statistics, Data Analysis, and Probability 1.1 Know the concepts of mean, median, and mode; compute and compare simple examples to show that they may differ.

Statistics, Data Analysis, and Probability 1.4 Identify ordered pairs of data from a graph and interpret the meaning of the data in terms of the situation depicted by the graph.

Page 350

Algebra and Functions 1.0 Students use variables in simple expressions, compute the value of the expression for specific values of the variable, and plot and interpret the results.

Algebra and Functions 1.1 Use information taken from a graph or equation to answer questions about a problem situation.

Algebra and Functions 1.2 Use a letter to represent an unknown number; write and evaluate simple algebraic expressions in one variable by substitution.

Algebra and Functions 1.5 Solve problems involving linear functions with integer values; write the equation; and graph the resulting ordered pairs of integers on a grid.

Statistics, Data Analysis, and Probability 1.4 Identify ordered pairs of data from a graph and interpret the meaning of the data in terms of the situation depicted by the graph.

Mathematical Reasoning 2.3 Use a variety of methods, such as words, numbers, symbols, charts, graphs, tables, diagrams, and models, to explain mathematical reasoning.

Mathematical Reasoning 3.0 Students move beyond a particular problem by generalizing to other situations.

Page 351

Algebra and Functions 1.0 Students use variables in simple expressions, compute the value of the expression for specific values of the variable, and plot and interpret the results.

Algebra and Functions 1.1 Use information taken from a graph or equation to answer questions about a problem situation.

Algebra and Functions 1.2 Use a letter to represent an unknown number; write and evaluate simple algebraic expressions in one variable by substitution.

Pages 354, 355

Algebra and Functions 1.0 Students use variables in simple expressions, compute the value of the expression for specific values of the variable, and plot and interpret the results.

Algebra and Functions 1.1 Use information taken from a graph or equation to answer questions about a problem situation.

Algebra and Functions 1.2 Use a letter to represent an unknown number; write and evaluate simple algebraic expressions in one variable by substitution.

Algebra and Functions 1.5 Solve problems involving linear functions with integer values; write the equation; and graph the resulting ordered pairs of integers on a grid.

Statistics, Data Analysis, and Probability 1.4 Identify ordered pairs of data from a graph and interpret the meaning of the data in terms of the situation depicted by the graph.

Statistics, Data Analysis, and Probability 1.5 Know how to write ordered pairs correctly; for example (x,y).

Mathematical Reasoning 2.3 Use a variety of methods, such as words, numbers, symbols, charts, graphs, tables, diagrams, and models, to explain mathematical reasoning.

Page 355

Algebra and Functions 1.0 Students use variables in simple expressions, compute the value of the expression for specific values of the variable, and plot and interpret the results.

Algebra and Functions 1.1 Use information taken from a graph or equation to answer questions about a problem situation.

Algebra and Functions 1.5 Solve problems involving linear functions with integer values; write the equation; and graph the resulting ordered pairs of integers on a grid.

Statistics, Data Analysis, and Probability 1.4 Identify ordered pairs of data from a graph and interpret the meaning of the data in terms of the situation depicted by the graph.

Page 356

Algebra and Functions 1.1 Use information taken from a graph or equation to answer questions about a problem situation.

Algebra and Functions 1.2 Use a letter to represent an unknown number; write and evaluate simple algebraic expressions in one variable by substitution.

Statistics, Data Analysis, and Probability 1.2 Organize and display single-variable data in appropriate graphs and representations (e.g., histogram, circle graphs) and explain which types of graphs are appropriate for various data sets.

Statistics, Data Analysis, and Probability 1.4 Identify ordered pairs of data from a graph and interpret the meaning of the data in terms of the situation depicted by the graph.

Pages 357, 358

Algebra and Functions 1.1 Use information taken from a graph or equation to answer questions about a problem situation.

Statistics, Data Analysis, and Probability 1.2 Organize and display single-variable data in appropriate graphs and representations (e.g., histogram, circle graphs) and explain which types of graphs are appropriate for various data sets.

Statistics, Data Analysis, and Probability 1.4 Identify ordered pairs of data from a graph and interpret the meaning of the data in terms of the situation depicted by the graph.

Page 360

Measurement and Geometry 1.0 Students understand and compute the volumes and areas of simple objects.

Measurement and Geometry 1.4 Differentiate between, and use appropriate units of measures for, two- and three-dimensional objects (i.e., find the perimeter, area, volume).

Mathematical Reasoning 2.4 Express the solution clearly and logically by using the appropriate mathematical notation and terms and clear language; support solutions with evidence in both verbal and symbolic work.

Page 361

Number Sense 1.0 Students compute with very large and very small numbers, positive integers, decimals, and fractions and understand the relationship between decimals, fractions, and percents. They understand the relative magnitudes of numbers.

Measurement and Geometry 2.0 Students identify, describe, and classify the properties of, and the relationships between, plane and solid geometric figures.

Statistics, Data Analysis, and Probability 1.1 Know the concepts of mean, median, and mode; compute and compare simple examples to show that they may differ.

Page 362

Number Sense 2.4 Understand the concept of multiplication and division of fractions.

Algebra and Functions 1.5 Solve problems involving linear functions with integer values; write the equation; and graph the resulting ordered pairs of integers on a grid.

Page 364

Measurement and Geometry 1.0 Students understand and compute the volumes and areas of simple objects.

Measurement and Geometry 1.4 Differentiate between, and use appropriate units of measures for, two- and three-dimensional objects (i.e., find the perimeter, area, volume).

Statistics, Data Analysis, and Probability 1.1 Know the concepts of mean, median, and mode; compute and compare simple examples to show that they may differ.

Page 365

Number Sense 1.0 Students compute with very large and very small numbers, positive integers, decimals, and fractions and understand the relationship between decimals, fractions, and percents. They understand the relative magnitudes of numbers.

Measurement and Geometry 1.0 Students understand and compute the volumes and areas of simple objects.

Measurement and Geometry 1.4 Differentiate between, and use appropriate units of measures for, two- and three-dimensional objects (i.e., find the perimeter, area, volume).

Statistics, Data Analysis, and Probability 1.1 Know the concepts of mean, median, and mode; compute and compare simple examples to show that they may differ.

Page 366

Measurement and Geometry 1.0 Students understand and compute the volumes and areas of simple objects.

Mathematical Reasoning 2.4 Express the solution clearly and logically by using the appropriate mathematical notation and terms and clear language; support solutions with evidence in both verbal and symbolic work.

Page 369–370

Measurement and Geometry 2.0 Students identify, describe, and classify the properties of, and the relationships between, plane and solid geometric figures.

Measurement and Geometry 2.3 Visualize and draw two-dimensional views of three-dimensional objects made from rectangular solids.

Pages 372, 373

Measurement and Geometry 2.0 Students identify, describe, and classify the properties of, and the relationships between, plane and solid geometric figures.

Measurement and Geometry 2.3 Visualize and draw two-dimensional views of three-dimensional objects made from rectangular solids.

Page 375

Measurement and Geometry 1.0 Students understand and compute the volumes and areas of simple objects.

Measurement and Geometry 1.3 Understand the concept of volume and use the appropriate units in common measuring systems (i.e., cubic centimeter [cm^3], cubic meter [m^3], cubic inch [$in.^3$], cubic yard [$yd.^3$]) to compute the volume of rectangular solids.

Measurement and Geometry 1.4 Differentiate between, and use appropriate units of measures for, two- and three-dimensional objects (i.e., find the perimeter, area, volume).

Page 377

Mathematical Reasoning 2.2 Apply strategies and results from simpler problems to more complex problems.

CA28

Page 379

Measurement and Geometry 1.0 Students understand and compute the volumes and areas of simple objects.

Measurement and Geometry 1.3 Understand the concept of volume and use the appropriate units in common measuring systems (i.e., cubic centimeter [cm^3], cubic meter [m^3], cubic inch [$in.^3$], cubic yard [$yd.^3$]) to compute the volume of rectangular solids.

Measurement and Geometry 1.4 Differentiate between, and use appropriate units of measures for, two- and three-dimensional objects (i.e., find the perimeter, area, volume).

Page 380

Measurement and Geometry 1.0 Students understand and compute the volumes and areas of simple objects.

Measurement and Geometry 1.4 Differentiate between, and use appropriate units of measures for, two- and three-dimensional objects (i.e., find the perimeter, area, volume).

Page 382

Measurement and Geometry 1.0 Students understand and compute the volumes and areas of simple objects.

Mathematical Reasoning 1.0 Students make decisions about how to approach problems.

Page 383

Measurement and Geometry 1.0 Students understand and compute the volumes and areas of simple objects.

Measurement and Geometry 1.3 Understand the concept of volume and use the appropriate units in common measuring systems (i.e., cubic centimeter [cm^3], cubic meter [m^3], cubic inch [$in.^3$], cubic yard [$yd.^3$]) to compute the volume of rectangular solids.

Measurement and Geometry 1.4 Differentiate between, and use appropriate units of measures for, two- and three-dimensional objects (i.e., find the perimeter, area, volume).

Mathematical Reasoning 2.2 Apply strategies and results from simpler problems to more complex problems.

Page 384

Statistics, Data Analysis, and Probability 1.0 Students display, analyze, compare, and interpret different data sets, including data sets of different sizes.

Measurement and Geometry 1.4 Differentiate between, and use appropriate units of measures for, two- and three-dimensional objects (i.e., find the perimeter, area, volume).

Pages 389

Measurement and Geometry 1.1 Derive and use the formula for the area of a triangle and of a parallelogram by comparing it with the formula for the area of a rectangle (i.e., two of the same triangles make a parallelogram with twice the area; a parallelogram is compared with a rectangle of the same area by cutting and pasting a right triangle on the parallelogram).

Measurement and Geometry 1.2 Construct a cube and rectangular box from two-dimensional patterns and use these patterns to compute the surface area for these objects.

Measurement and Geometry 1.4 Differentiate between, and use appropriate units of measures for, two- and three-dimensional objects (i.e., find the perimeter, area, volume).

Mathematical Reasoning 3.2 Note the method of deriving the solution and demonstrate a conceptual understanding of the derivation by solving similar problems.

Page 390

Measurement and Geometry 1.2 Construct a cube and rectangular box from two-dimensional patterns and use these patterns to compute the surface area for these objects.

Measurement and Geometry 1.4 Differentiate between, and use appropriate units of measures for, two- and three-dimensional objects (i.e., find the perimeter, area, volume).

Mathematical Reasoning 3.2 Note the method of deriving the solution and demonstrate a conceptual understanding of the derivation by solving similar problems.

Page 393

Number Sense 1.4 Determine the prime factors of all numbers through 50 and write the numbers as the product of their prime factors by using exponents to show multiples of a factor (e.g., $24 = 2 \times 2 \times 2 \times 3 = 2^3 \times 3$).

Pages 394, 395

Number Sense 1.4 Determine the prime factors of all numbers through 50 and write the numbers as the product of their prime factors by using exponents to show multiples of a factor (e.g., $24 = 2 \times 2 \times 2 \times 3 = 2^3 \times 3$).

Page 396

Number Sense 1.4 Determine the prime factors of all numbers through 50 and write the numbers as the product of their prime factors by using exponents to show multiples of a factor (e.g., $24 = 2 \times 2 \times 2 \times 3 = 2^3 \times 3$).

Page 398

Statistics, Data Analysis, and Probability 1.3 Use fractions and percentages to compare data sets of different sizes.

Page 399

Mathematical Reasoning 2.3 Use a variety of methods, such as words, numbers, symbols, charts, graphs, tables, diagrams, and models, to explain mathematical reasoning.

Pages 400, 401

Mathematical Reasoning 2.3 Use a variety of methods, such as words, numbers, symbols, charts, graphs, tables, diagrams, and models, to explain mathematical reasoning.

Page 402

Mathematical Reasoning 1.1 Analyze problems by identifying relationships, distinguishing relevant from irrelevant information, sequencing and prioritizing information, and observing patterns.

Page 404

Number Sense 1.2 Interpret percents as a part of a hundred; find decimals and percent equivalents for common fractions and explain why they represent the same value; compute a given percent of a whole number.

Statistics, Data Analysis, and Probability 1.3 Use fractions and percentages to compare data sets of different sizes.

Pages 405–406

Number Sense 1.2 Interpret percents as a part of a hundred; find decimals and percent equivalents for common fractions and explain why they represent the same value; compute a given percent of a whole number.

Mathematical Reasoning 1.1 Analyze problems by identifying relationships, distinguishing relevant from irrelevant information, sequencing and prioritizing information, and observing patterns.

Page 408

Mathematical Reasoning 2.3 Use a variety of methods, such as words, numbers, symbols, charts, graphs, tables, diagrams, and models, to explain mathematical reasoning.

Page 409

Mathematical Reasoning 2.3 Use a variety of methods, such as words, numbers, symbols, charts, graphs, tables, diagrams, and models, to explain mathematical reasoning.

Page 410

Mathematical Reasoning 2.3 Use a variety of methods, such as words, numbers, symbols, charts, graphs, tables, diagrams, and models, to explain mathematical reasoning.

Pages 412, 413

Algebra and Functions (1.2) Use a letter to represent an unknown number; write and evaluate simple algebraic expressions in one variable by substitution.

Page 414

Measurement and Geometry (2.1) Measure, identify, and draw angles, perpendicular and parallel lines, rectangles, and triangles by using appropriate tools (e.g., straightedge, ruler, compass, protractor, drawing software).

Page 416

Mathematical Reasoning 2.2 Apply strategies and results from simpler problems to more complex problems.

Page 418

Algebra and Functions 1.1 Use information taken from a graph or equation to answer questions about a problem situation.

Algebra and Functions (1.5) Solve problems involving linear functions with integer values; write the equation; and graph the resulting ordered pairs of integers on a grid.

Statistics, Data Analysis, and Probability 1.0 Students display, analyze, compare, and interpret different data sets, including data sets of different sizes.

Statistics, Data Analysis, and Probability (1.4) Identify ordered pairs of data from a graph and interpret the meaning of the data in terms of the situation depicted by the graph.

Page 419

Algebra and Functions 1.1 Use information taken from a graph or equation to answer questions about a problem situation.

Algebra and Functions (1.5) Solve problems involving linear functions with integer values; write the equation; and graph the resulting ordered pairs of integers on a grid.

Statistics, Data Analysis, and Probability 1.0 Students display, analyze, compare, and interpret different data sets, including data sets of different sizes.

Statistics, Data Analysis, and Probability 1.1 Know the concepts of mean, median, and mode; compute and compare simple examples to show that they may differ.

Statistics, Data Analysis, and Probability (1.4) Identify ordered pairs of data from a graph and interpret the meaning of the data in terms of the situation depicted by the graph.

Page 420

Statistics, Data Analysis, and Probability 1.0 Students display, analyze, compare, and interpret different data sets, including data sets of different sizes.

Statistics, Data Analysis, and Probability 1.1 Know the concepts of mean, median, and mode; compute and compare simple examples to show that they may differ.

Page 421

Algebra and Functions 1.1 Use information taken from a graph or equation to answer questions about a problem situation.

Page 423

Mathematical Reasoning 1.1 Analyze problems by identifying relationships, distinguishing relevant from irrelevant information, sequencing and prioritizing information, and observing patterns.

Pages 424, 425

Mathematical Reasoning 1.1 Analyze problems by identifying relationships, distinguishing relevant from irrelevant information, sequencing and prioritizing information, and observing patterns.

Pages CA2–CA4

Measurement and Geometry (2.1) Measure, identify, and draw angles, perpendicular and parallel lines, rectangles, and triangles by using appropriate tools (e.g., straightedge, ruler, compass, protractor, drawing software).

Pages CA5, CA6

Measurement and Geometry 2.3 Visualize and draw two-dimensional views of three-dimensional objects made from rectangular solids.

Pages CA7, CA8

Algebra and Functions 1.3 Know and use the distributive property in equations and expressions with variables.

Mathematical Reasoning 1.2 Determine when and how to break a problem into simpler parts.

Pages CA9–CA17

Number Sense (2.2) Demonstrate proficiency with division, including division with positive decimals and long division with multidigit divisors.

Pages CA18–CA21

Number Sense 2.4 Understand the concept of multiplication and division of fractions.

Number Sense 2.5 Compute and perform simple multiplication and division of fractions and apply these procedures to solving problems.

Math Boxes 7•1

1. **Number Sense 2.4** Understand the concept of multiplication and division of fractions.

2. **Number Sense 2.3** Solve simple problems, including ones arising in concrete situations, involving the addition and subtraction of fractions and mixed numbers (like and unlike denominators of 20 or less), and express answers in the simplest form.

3. **Number Sense 2.4** Understand the concept of multiplication and division of fractions.

4. **Mathematical Reasoning 1.1** Analyze problems by identifying relationships, distinguishing relevant from irrelevant information, sequencing and prioritizing information, and observing patterns.

5. **Number Sense 2.0** Students perform calculations and solve problems involving addition, subtraction, and simple multiplication and division of fractions and decimals.

6. **Number Sense 2.3** Solve simple problems, including ones arising in concrete situations, involving the addition and subtraction of fractions and mixed numbers (like and unlike denominators of 20 or less), and express answers in the simplest form.

Math Boxes 7•2

1. **Measurement and Geometry 1.4** Differentiate between, and use appropriate units of measures for, two- and three-dimensional objects (i.e., find the perimeter, area, volume).

2. **Statistics, Data Analysis, and Probability 1.1** Know the concepts of mean, median, and mode; compute and compare simple examples to show that they may differ.

3. **Measurement and Geometry 2.1** Measure, identify, and draw angles, perpendicular and parallel lines, rectangles, and triangles by using appropriate tools (e.g., straightedge, ruler, compass, protractor, drawing software).

4. **Number Sense 1.2** Interpret percents as part of a hundred; find decimal and percent equivalents for common fractions and explain why they represent the same value; compute a given percent of a whole number.

Math Boxes 7•3

1. **Number Sense 2.4** Understand the concept of multiplication and division of fractions.

2. **Number Sense 2.3** Solve simple problems, including ones arising in concrete situations, involving the addition and subtraction of fractions and mixed numbers (like and unlike denominators of 20 or less), and express answers in the simplest form.

3. **Number Sense 2.4** Understand the concept of multiplication and division of fractions.

4. **Mathematical Reasoning 1.1** Analyze problems by identifying relationships, distinguishing relevant from irrelevant information, sequencing and prioritizing information, and observing patterns.

5. **Number Sense 2.0** Students perform calculations and solve problems involving addition, subtraction, and simple multiplication and division of fractions and decimals.

6. **Number Sense 2.3** Solve simple problems, including ones arising in concrete situations, involving the addition and subtraction of fractions and mixed numbers (like and unlike denominators of 20 or less), and express answers in the simplest form.

Math Boxes 7•4

1. **Measurement and Geometry 1.4** Differentiate between, and use appropriate units of measures for, two- and three-dimensional objects (i.e., find the perimeter, area, volume).

2. **Statistics, Data Analysis, and Probability 1.1** Know the concepts of mean, median, and mode; compute and compare simple examples to show that they may differ.

3. **Measurement and Geometry 2.1** Measure, identify, and draw angles, perpendicular and parallel lines, rectangles, and triangles by using appropriate tools (e.g., straightedge, ruler, compass, protractor, drawing software).

4. **Number Sense 1.2** Interpret percents as part of a hundred; find decimal and percent equivalents for common fractions and explain why they represent the same value; compute a given percent of a whole number.

Math Boxes 7•5

1. **Mathematical Reasoning 2.0** Students use strategies, skills, and concepts in finding solutions.

2. **Number Sense 2.1** Add, subtract, multiply, and divide with decimals; add with negative integers; subtract positive integers from negative integers; and verify the reasonableness of the results.

3. **Number Sense 1.3** Understand and compute positive integer powers of nonnegative integers; compute examples as repeated multiplication.

4. **Algebra and Functions 1.1** Use information taken from a graph or equation to answer questions about a problem situation.

5. **Number Sense 1.5** Identify and represent on a number line decimals, fractions, mixed numbers, and positive and negative integers.

6. **Number Sense 2.5** Compute and perform simple multiplication and division of fractions and apply these procedures to solving problems.

Math Boxes 7•6

1. **Measurement and Geometry 1.4** Differentiate between, and use appropriate units of measures for, two- and three-dimensional objects (i.e., find the perimeter, area, volume).

Math Boxes 7♦6 *cont.*

2. Statistics, Data Analysis, and Probability 1.1 Know the concepts of mean, median, and mode; compute and compare simple examples to show that they may differ.

3. Measurement and Geometry 2.1 Measure, identify, and draw angles, perpendicular and parallel lines, rectangles, and triangles by using appropriate tools (e.g., straightedge, ruler, compass, protractor, drawing software).

4. Number Sense 1.2 Interpret percents as part of a hundred; find decimal and percent equivalents for common fractions and explain why they represent the same value; compute a given percent of a whole number.

Math Boxes 7♦7

1. Mathematical Reasoning 2.3 Use a variety of methods, such as words, numbers, symbols, charts, graphs, tables, diagrams, and models, to explain mathematical reasoning.

2. Algebra and Functions 1.3 Know and use the distributive property in equations and expressions with variables.

3. Number Sense 1.5 Identify and represent on a number line decimals, fractions, mixed numbers, and positive and negative integers.

4. Mathematical Reasoning 1.1 Analyze problems by identifying relationships, distinguishing relevant from irrelevant information, sequencing and prioritizing information, and observing patterns.

5. Number Sense 2.0 Students perform calculations and solve problems involving addition, subtraction, and simple multiplication and division of fractions and decimals.

6. Number Sense 2.5 Compute and perform simple multiplication and division of fractions and apply these procedures to solving problems.

Math Boxes 7♦8

1. Mathematical Reasoning 2.0 Students use strategies, skills, and concepts in finding solutions.

2. Number Sense 2.1 Add, subtract, multiply, and divide with decimals; add with negative integers; subtract positive integers from negative integers; and verify the reasonableness of the results.

3. Number Sense 1.3 Understand and compute positive integer powers of nonnegative integers; compute examples as repeated multiplication.

4. Algebra and Functions 1.1 Use information taken from a graph or equation to answer questions about a problem situation.

5. Number Sense 1.5 Identify and represent on a number line decimals, fractions, mixed numbers, and positive and negative integers.

6. Number Sense 2.5 Compute and perform simple multiplication and division of fractions and apply these procedures to solving problems.

Math Boxes 7♦9

1. Mathematical Reasoning 1.2 Determine when and how to break a problem into simpler parts.

2. Algebra and Functions 1.2 Use a letter to represent an unknown number; write and evaluate simple algebraic expressions in one variable by substitution.

3. Mathematical Reasoning 2.6 Make precise calculations and check the validity of the results from the context of the problem.

4. Mathematical Reasoning 1.2 Determine when and how to break a problem into simpler parts.

5. Number Sense 2.1 Add, subtract, multiply, and divide with decimals; add with negative integers; subtract positive integers from negative integers; and verify the reasonableness of the results.

6. Number Sense 1.5 Identify and represent on a number line decimals, fractions, mixed numbers, and positive and negative integers.

Math Boxes 7♦10

1. Mathematical Reasoning 2.3 Use a variety of methods, such as words, numbers, symbols, charts, graphs, tables, diagrams, and models, to explain mathematical reasoning.

2. Algebra and Functions 1.3 Know and use the distributive property in equations and expressions with variables.

3. Number Sense 1.5 Identify and represent on a number line decimals, fractions, mixed numbers, and positive and negative integers.

4. Mathematical Reasoning 1.1 Analyze problems by identifying relationships, distinguishing relevant from irrelevant information, sequencing and prioritizing information, and observing patterns.

5. Number Sense 2.0 Students perform calculations and solve problems involving addition, subtraction, and simple multiplication and division of fractions and decimals.

6. Number Sense 2.5 Compute and perform simple multiplication and division of fractions and apply these procedures to solving problems.

Math Boxes 7♦11

1. Mathematical Reasoning 1.2 Determine when and how to break a problem into simpler parts.

2. Algebra and Functions 1.2 Use a letter to represent an unknown number; write and evaluate simple algebraic expressions in one variable by substitution.

3. Mathematical Reasoning 2.6 Make precise calculations and check the validity of the results from the context of the problem.

4. Mathematical Reasoning 1.2 Determine when and how to break a problem into simpler parts.

5. Number Sense 2.1 Add, subtract, multiply, and divide with decimals; add with negative integers; subtract positive integers from negative integers; and verify the reasonableness of the results.

6. Number Sense 1.5 Identify and represent on a number line decimals, fractions, mixed numbers, and positive and negative integers.

Math Boxes 7♦12

1. Number Sense 2.5 Compute and perform simple multiplication and division of fractions and apply these procedures to solving problems.

Math Boxes 7•12 *cont.*

2. **Number Sense (2.3)** Solve simple problems, including ones arising in concrete situations, involving the addition and subtraction of fractions and mixed numbers (like and unlike denominators of 20 or less), and express answers in the simplest form.

3. **Number Sense 2.4** Understand the concept of multiplication and division of fractions.

4. **Algebra and Functions 1.3** Know and use the distributive property in equations and expressions with variables.

5. **Number Sense 2.5** Compute and perform simple multiplication and division of fractions and apply these procedures to solving problems.

6. **Number Sense (1.5)** Identify and represent on a number line decimals, fractions, mixed numbers, and positive and negative integers.

Math Boxes 8•1

1. **Number Sense (1.2)** Interpret percents as part of a hundred; find decimal and percent equivalents for common fractions and explain why they represent the same value; compute a given percent of a whole number.

2. **Mathematical Reasoning 2.3** Use a variety of methods, such as words, numbers, symbols, charts, graphs, tables, diagrams, and models, to explain mathematical reasoning.

3. **Number Sense 2.4** Understand the concept of multiplication and division of fractions.

4. **Mathematical Reasoning 1.1** Analyze problems by identifying relationships, distinguishing relevant from irrelevant information, sequencing and prioritizing information, and observing patterns.

5. **Measurement and Geometry 1.4** Differentiate between, and use appropriate units of measures for, two- and three-dimensional objects (i.e., find the perimeter, area, volume).

Math Boxes 8•2

1. **Number Sense (2.3)** Solve simple problems, including ones arising in concrete situations, involving the addition and subtraction of fractions and mixed numbers (like and unlike denominators of 20 or less), and express answers in the simplest form.

2. **Mathematical Reasoning 1.1** Analyze problems by identifying relationships, distinguishing relevant from irrelevant information, sequencing and prioritizing information, and observing patterns.

3. **Mathematical Reasoning 1.1** Analyze problems by identifying relationships, distinguishing relevant from irrelevant information, sequencing and prioritizing information, and observing patterns.

4. **Mathematical Reasoning 2.3** Use a variety of methods, such as words, numbers, symbols, charts, graphs, tables, diagrams, and models, to explain mathematical reasoning.

5. **Algebra and Functions (1.2)** Use a letter to represent an unknown number; write and evaluate simple algebraic expressions in one variable by substitution.

6. **Mathematical Reasoning 2.3** Use a variety of methods, such as words, numbers, symbols, charts, graphs, tables, diagrams, and models, to explain mathematical reasoning.

Math Boxes 8•3

1. **Number Sense (1.2)** Interpret percents as part of a hundred; find decimal and percent equivalents for common fractions and explain why they represent the same value; compute a given percent of a whole number.

2. **Mathematical Reasoning 2.3** Use a variety of methods, such as words, numbers, symbols, charts, graphs, tables, diagrams, and models, to explain mathematical reasoning.

3. **Number Sense 2.4** Understand the concept of multiplication and division of fractions.

4. **Mathematical Reasoning 1.1** Analyze problems by identifying relationships, distinguishing relevant from irrelevant information, sequencing and prioritizing information, and observing patterns.

5. **Measurement and Geometry 1.4** Differentiate between, and use appropriate units of measures for, two- and three-dimensional objects (i.e., find the perimeter, area, volume).

Math Boxes 8•4

1. **Number Sense (2.3)** Solve simple problems, including ones arising in concrete situations, involving the addition and subtraction of fractions and mixed numbers (like and unlike denominators of 20 or less), and express answers in the simplest form.

2. **Mathematical Reasoning 1.1** Analyze problems by identifying relationships, distinguishing relevant from irrelevant information, sequencing and prioritizing information, and observing patterns.

3. **Mathematical Reasoning 1.1** Analyze problems by identifying relationships, distinguishing relevant from irrelevant information, sequencing and prioritizing information, and observing patterns.

4. **Mathematical Reasoning 2.3** Use a variety of methods, such as words, numbers, symbols, charts, graphs, tables, diagrams, and models, to explain mathematical reasoning.

5. **Algebra and Functions (1.2)** Use a letter to represent an unknown number; write and evaluate simple algebraic expressions in one variable by substitution.

6. **Mathematical Reasoning 2.3** Use a variety of methods, such as words, numbers, symbols, charts, graphs, tables, diagrams, and models, to explain mathematical reasoning.

Math Boxes 8•5

1. **Number Sense 2.4** Understand the concept of multiplication and division of fractions.

2. **Algebra and Functions 1.3** Know and use the distributive property in equations and expressions with variables.

3. **Algebra and Functions 1.1** Use information taken from a graph or equation to answer questions about a problem situation.

CA33

Math Boxes 8◆5 cont.

4. **Measurement and Geometry** 2.1 Measure, identify, and draw angles, perpendicular and parallel lines, rectangles, and triangles by using appropriate tools (e.g., straightedge, ruler, compass, protractor, drawing software).

5. **Measurement and Geometry** 2.0 Students identify, describe, and classify the properties of, and the relationships between, plane and solid geometric figures.

Math Boxes 8◆6

1. **Mathematical Reasoning** 2.4 Express the solution clearly and logically by using the appropriate mathematical notation and terms and clear language; support solutions with evidence in both verbal and symbolic work.

2. **Number Sense** 2.4 Understand the concept of multiplication and division of fractions.

3. **Number Sense** 2.3 Solve simple problems, including ones arising in concrete situations, involving the addition and subtraction of fractions and mixed numbers (like and unlike denominators of 20 or less), and express answers in the simplest form.

4. **Number Sense** 2.4 Understand the concept of multiplication and division of fractions.

5. **Measurement and Geometry** 2.1 Measure, identify, and draw angles, perpendicular and parallel lines, rectangles, and triangles by using appropriate tools (e.g., straightedge, ruler, compass, protractor, drawing software).

Math Boxes 8◆7

1. **Number Sense** 2.4 Understand the concept of multiplication and division of fractions.

2. **Algebra and Functions** 1.3 Know and use the distributive property in equations and expressions with variables.

3. **Algebra and Functions** 1.1 Use information taken from a graph or equation to answer questions about a problem situation.

4. **Measurement and Geometry** 2.1 Measure, identify, and draw angles, perpendicular and parallel lines, rectangles, and triangles by using appropriate tools (e.g., straightedge, ruler, compass, protractor, drawing software).

5. **Measurement and Geometry** 2.0 Students identify, describe, and classify the properties of, and the relationships between, plane and solid geometric figures.

Math Boxes 8◆8

1. **Mathematical Reasoning** 2.4 Express the solution clearly and logically by using the appropriate mathematical notation and terms and clear language; support solutions with evidence in both verbal and symbolic work.

2. **Number Sense** 2.4 Understand the concept of multiplication and division of fractions.

3. **Number Sense** 2.3 Solve simple problems, including ones arising in concrete situations, involving the addition and subtraction of fractions and mixed numbers (like and unlike denominators of 20 or less), and express answers in the simplest form.

4. **Number Sense** 2.4 Understand the concept of multiplication and division of fractions.

5. **Measurement and Geometry** 2.1 Measure, identify, and draw angles, perpendicular and parallel lines, rectangles, and triangles by using appropriate tools (e.g., straightedge, ruler, compass, protractor, drawing software).

Math Boxes 8◆9

1. **Number Sense** 2.5 Compute and perform simple multiplication and division of fractions and apply these procedures to solving problems.

2. **Measurement and Geometry** 1.4 Differentiate between, and use appropriate units of measures for, two- and three-dimensional objects (i.e., find the perimeter, area, volume).

3. **Number Sense** 2.2 Demonstrate proficiency with division, including division with positive decimals and long division with multidigit divisors.

4. **Mathematical Reasoning** 2.4 Express the solution clearly and logically by using the appropriate mathematical notation and terms and clear language; support solutions with evidence in both verbal and symbolic work.

5. **Algebra and Functions** 1.1 Use information taken from a graph or equation to answer questions about a problem situation.

Math Boxes 8◆10

1. **Number Sense** 2.5 Compute and perform simple multiplication and division of fractions and apply these procedures to solving problems.

2. **Number Sense** 1.2 Interpret percents as part of a hundred; find decimal and percent equivalents for common fractions and explain why they represent the same value; compute a given percent of a whole number.

3. **Number Sense** 2.3 Solve simple problems, including ones arising in concrete situations, involving the addition and subtraction of fractions and mixed numbers (like and unlike denominators of 20 or less), and express answers in the simplest form.

4. **Number Sense** 2.5 Compute and perform simple multiplication and division of fractions and apply these procedures to solving problems.

5. **Mathematical Reasoning** 2.2 Apply strategies and results from simpler problems to more complex problems.

6. **Mathematical Reasoning** 1.0 Students make decisions about how to approach problems.

Math Boxes 8◆11

1. **Number Sense** 2.5 Compute and perform simple multiplication and division of fractions and apply these procedures to solving problems.

2. **Measurement and Geometry** 1.4 Differentiate between, and use appropriate units of measures for, two- and three-dimensional objects (i.e., find the perimeter, area, volume).

3. **Number Sense** 2.2 Demonstrate proficiency with division, including division with positive decimals and long division with multidigit divisors.

4. **Mathematical Reasoning** 2.4 Express the solution clearly and logically by using the appropriate mathematical notation and terms and clear language; support solutions with evidence in both verbal and symbolic work.

5. **Algebra and Functions** 1.1 Use information taken from a graph or equation to answer questions about a problem situation.

Math Boxes 8⋅12

1. **Number Sense 2.5** Compute and perform simple multiplication and division of fractions and apply these procedures to solving problems.
2. **Number Sense 1.2** Interpret percents as part of a hundred; find decimal and percent equivalents for common fractions and explain why they represent the same value; compute a given percent of a whole number.
3. **Number Sense 2.3** Solve simple problems, including ones arising in concrete situations, involving the addition and subtraction of fractions and mixed numbers (like and unlike denominators of 20 or less), and express answers in the simplest form.
4. **Number Sense 2.5** Compute and perform simple multiplication and division of fractions and apply these procedures to solving problems.
5. **Mathematical Reasoning 2.2** Apply strategies and results from simpler problems to more complex problems.
6. **Mathematical Reasoning 1.0** Students make decisions about how to approach problems.

Math Boxes 8⋅13

1. **Measurement and Geometry 1.4** Differentiate between, and use appropriate units of measures for, two- and three-dimensional objects (i.e., find the perimeter, area, volume).
2. **Measurement and Geometry 2.1** Measure, identify, and draw angles, perpendicular and parallel lines, rectangles, and triangles by using appropriate tools (e.g., straightedge, ruler, compass, protractor, drawing software).
3. **Measurement and Geometry 1.4** Differentiate between, and use appropriate units of measures for, two- and three-dimensional objects (i.e., find the perimeter, area, volume).
4. **Measurement and Geometry 2.2** Know that the sum of the angles of any triangle is 180° and the sum of the angles of any quadrilateral is 360° and use this information to solve problems.
5. **Mathematical Reasoning 2.3** Use a variety of methods, such as words, numbers, symbols, charts, graphs, tables, diagrams, and models, to explain mathematical reasoning.

Math Boxes 9⋅1

1. **Measurement and Geometry 2.0** Students identify, describe, and classify the properties of, and the relationships between, plane and solid geometric figures.
2. **Number Sense 2.4** Understand the concept of multiplication and division of fractions.
3. **Measurement and Geometry 1.3** Understand the concept of volume and use the appropriate units in common measuring systems (i.e., cubic centimeter [cm³], cubic meter [m³], cubic inch [in.³], cubic yard [yd.³]) to compute the volume of rectangular solids.
4. **Number Sense 1.2** Interpret percents as part of a hundred; find decimal and percent equivalents for common fractions and explain why they represent the same value; compute a given percent of a whole number.
5. **Number Sense 2.3** Solve simple problems, including ones arising in concrete situations, involving the addition and subtraction of fractions and mixed numbers (like and unlike denominators of 20 or less), and express answers in the simplest form.
6. **Number Sense 1.4** Determine the prime factors of all numbers through 50 and write the numbers as the product of their prime factors by using exponents to show multiples of a factor (e.g., $24 = 2 \times 2 \times 2 \times 3 = 2^3 \times 3$).

Math Boxes 9⋅2

1. **Number Sense 2.5** Compute and perform simple multiplication and division of fractions and apply these procedures to solving problems.
2. **Measurement and Geometry 1.3** Understand the concept of volume and use the appropriate units in common measuring systems (i.e., cubic centimeter [cm³], cubic meter [m³], cubic inch [in.³], cubic yard [yd.³]) to compute the volume of rectangular solids.
3. **Number Sense 1.5** Identify and represent on a number line decimals, fractions, mixed numbers, and positive and negative integers.
4. **Mathematical Reasoning 1.0** Students make decisions about how to approach problems.
5. **Number Sense 2.2** Demonstrate proficiency with division, including division with positive decimals and long division with multidigit divisors.
6. **Mathematical Reasoning 1.1** Analyze problems by identifying relationships, distinguishing relevant from irrelevant information, sequencing and prioritizing information, and observing patterns.

Math Boxes 9⋅3

1. **Measurement and Geometry 2.0** Students identify, describe, and classify the properties of, and the relationships between, plane and solid geometric figures.
2. **Number Sense 2.4** Understand the concept of multiplication and division of fractions.
3. **Measurement and Geometry 1.3** Understand the concept of volume and use the appropriate units in common measuring systems (i.e., cubic centimeter [cm³], cubic meter [m³], cubic inch [in.³], cubic yard [yd.³]) to compute the volume of rectangular solids.
4. **Number Sense 1.2** Interpret percents as part of a hundred; find decimal and percent equivalents for common fractions and explain why they represent the same value; compute a given percent of a whole number.
5. **Number Sense 2.3** Solve simple problems, including ones arising in concrete situations, involving the addition and subtraction of fractions and mixed numbers (like and unlike denominators of 20 or less), and express answers in the simplest form.

Math Boxes 9⋅4

1. **Number Sense 2.5** Compute and perform simple multiplication and division of fractions and apply these procedures to solving problems.
2. **Measurement and Geometry 1.3** Understand the concept of volume and use the appropriate units in common measuring systems (i.e., cubic centimeter [cm³], cubic meter [m³], cubic inch [in.³], cubic yard [yd.³]) to compute the volume of rectangular solids.
3. **Number Sense 1.5** Identify and represent on a number line decimals, fractions, mixed numbers, and positive and negative integers.
4. **Mathematical Reasoning 1.0** Students make decisions about how to approach problems.
5. **Number Sense 2.2** Demonstrate proficiency with division, including division with positive decimals and long division with multidigit divisors.

Math Boxes 9•4 *cont.*

6. **Mathematical Reasoning 1.1** Analyze problems by identifying relationships, distinguishing relevant from irrelevant information, sequencing and prioritizing information, and observing patterns.

Math Boxes 9•5

1. **Statistics, Data Analysis, and Probability 1.4** Identify ordered pairs of data from a graph and interpret the meaning of the data in terms of the situation depicted by the graph.

2. **Measurement and Geometry 1.4** Differentiate between, and use appropriate units of measures for, two- and three-dimensional objects (i.e., find the perimeter, area, volume).

3. **Mathematical Reasoning 1.0** Students make decisions about how to approach problems.

4. **Number Sense 1.5** Identify and represent on a number line decimals, fractions, mixed numbers, and positive and negative integers.

5. **Mathematical Reasoning 2.3** Use a variety of methods, such as words, numbers, symbols, charts, graphs, tables, diagrams, and models, to explain mathematical reasoning.

Math Boxes 9•6

1. **Mathematical Reasoning 2.3** Use a variety of methods, such as words, numbers, symbols, charts, graphs, tables, diagrams, and models, to explain mathematical reasoning.

2. **Measurement and Geometry 2.1** Measure, identify, and draw angles, perpendicular and parallel lines, rectangles, and triangles by using appropriate tools (e.g., straightedge, ruler, compass, protractor, drawing software).

3. **Mathematical Reasoning 2.3** Use a variety of methods, such as words, numbers, symbols, charts, graphs, tables, diagrams, and models, to explain mathematical reasoning.

4. **Measurement and Geometry 1.4** Differentiate between, and use appropriate units of measures for, two- and three-dimensional objects (i.e., find the perimeter, area, volume).

5. **Mathematical Reasoning 1.1** Analyze problems by identifying relationships, distinguishing relevant from irrelevant information, sequencing and prioritizing information, and observing patterns.

Math Boxes 9•7

1. **Statistics, Data Analysis, and Probability 1.4** Identify ordered pairs of data from a graph and interpret the meaning of the data in terms of the situation depicted by the graph.

2. **Measurement and Geometry 1.4** Differentiate between, and use appropriate units of measures for, two- and three-dimensional objects (i.e., find the perimeter, area, volume).

3. **Mathematical Reasoning 1.0** Students make decisions about how to approach problems.

4. **Number Sense 1.5** Identify and represent on a number line decimals, fractions, mixed numbers, and positive and negative integers.

5. **Mathematical Reasoning 2.3** Use a variety of methods, such as words, numbers, symbols, charts, graphs, tables, diagrams, and models, to explain mathematical reasoning.

Math Boxes 9•8

1. **Number Sense 2.1** Add, subtract, multiply, and divide with decimals; add with negative integers; subtract positive integers from negative integers; and verify the reasonableness of the results.

2. **Mathematical Reasoning 1.1** Analyze problems by identifying relationships, distinguishing relevant from irrelevant information, sequencing and prioritizing information, and observing patterns.

3. **Number Sense 2.2** Demonstrate proficiency with division, including division with positive decimals and long division with multidigit divisors.

4. **Statistics, Data Analysis, and Probability 1.1** Know the concepts of mean, median, and mode; compute and compare simple examples to show that they may differ.

5. **Algebra and Functions 1.1** Use information taken from a graph or equation to answer questions about a problem situation.

Math Boxes 9•9

1. **Mathematical Reasoning 2.3** Use a variety of methods, such as words, numbers, symbols, charts, graphs, tables, diagrams, and models, to explain mathematical reasoning.

2. **Measurement and Geometry 2.1** Measure, identify, and draw angles, perpendicular and parallel lines, rectangles, and triangles by using appropriate tools (e.g., straightedge, ruler, compass, protractor, drawing software).

3. **Mathematical Reasoning 2.3** Use a variety of methods, such as words, numbers, symbols, charts, graphs, tables, diagrams, and models, to explain mathematical reasoning.

4. **Measurement and Geometry 1.4** Differentiate between, and use appropriate units of measures for, two- and three-dimensional objects (i.e., find the perimeter, area, volume).

5. **Mathematical Reasoning 1.1** Analyze problems by identifying relationships, distinguishing relevant from irrelevant information, sequencing and prioritizing information, and observing patterns.

Math Boxes 9•10

1. **Number Sense 2.1** Add, subtract, multiply, and divide with decimals; add with negative integers; subtract positive integers from negative integers; and verify the reasonableness of the results.

2. **Mathematical Reasoning 1.1** Analyze problems by identifying relationships, distinguishing relevant from irrelevant information, sequencing and prioritizing information, and observing patterns.

3. **Number Sense 2.2** Demonstrate proficiency with division, including division with positive decimals and long division with multidigit divisors.

Math Boxes 9•10 *cont.*

4. Statistics, Data Analysis, and Probability 1.1 Know the concepts of mean, median, and mode; compute and compare simple examples to show that they may differ.

5. Algebra and Functions 1.1 Use information taken from a graph or equation to answer questions about a problem situation.

Math Boxes 9•11

1. Measurement and Geometry 1.3 Understand the concept of volume and use the appropriate units in common measuring systems (i.e., cubic centimeter [cm^3], cubic meter [m^3], cubic inch [$in.^3$], cubic yard [$yd.^3$]) to compute the volume of rectangular solids.

2. Mathematical Reasoning 2.5 Indicate the relative advantages of exact and approximate solutions to problems and give answers to a specified degree of accuracy.

3. Algebra and Functions 1.1 Use information taken from a graph or equation to answer questions about a problem situation.

4. Mathematical Reasoning 2.5 Indicate the relative advantages of exact and approximate solutions to problems and give answers to a specified degree of accuracy.

5. Measurement and Geometry 1.4 Differentiate between, and use appropriate units of measures for, two- and three-dimensional objects (i.e., find the perimeter, area, volume).

6. Mathematical Reasoning 2.2 Apply strategies and results from simpler problems to more complex problems.

Math Boxes 10•1

1. Statistics, Data Analysis, and Probability 1.4 Identify ordered pairs of data from a graph and interpret the meaning of the data in terms of the situation depicted by the graph.

2. Number Sense 2.1 Add, subtract, multiply, and divide with decimals; add with negative integers; subtract positive integers from negative integers; and verify the reasonableness of the results.

3. Mathematical Reasoning 2.0 Students use strategies, skills, and concepts in finding solutions.

4. Measurement and Geometry 1.4 Differentiate between, and use appropriate units of measures for, two- and three-dimensional objects (i.e., find the perimeter, area, volume).

5. Measurement and Geometry 1.3 Understand the concept of volume and use the appropriate units in common measuring systems (i.e., cubic centimeter [cm^3], cubic meter [m^3], cubic inch [$in.^3$], cubic yard [$yd.^3$]) to compute the volume of rectangular solids.

Math Boxes 10•2

1. Mathematical Reasoning 2.1 Use estimation to verify the reasonableness of calculated results.

2. Mathematical Reasoning 2.0 Students use strategies, skills, and concepts in finding solutions.

3. Number Sense 1.5 Identify and represent on a number line decimals, fractions, mixed numbers, and positive and negative integers.

4. Measurement and Geometry 1.4 Differentiate between, and use appropriate units of measures for, two- and three-dimensional objects (i.e., find the perimeter, area, volume).

5. Measurement and Geometry 1.3 Understand the concept of volume and use the appropriate units in common measuring systems (i.e., cubic centimeter [cm^3], cubic meter [m^3], cubic inch [$in.^3$], cubic yard [$yd.^3$]) to compute the volume of rectangular solids.

Math Boxes 10•3

1. Statistics, Data Analysis, and Probability 1.4 Identify ordered pairs of data from a graph and interpret the meaning of the data in terms of the situation depicted by the graph.

2. Number Sense 2.1 Add, subtract, multiply, and divide with decimals; add with negative integers; subtract positive integers from negative integers; and verify the reasonableness of the results.

3. Mathematical Reasoning 2.0 Students use strategies, skills, and concepts in finding solutions.

4. Measurement and Geometry 1.4 Differentiate between, and use appropriate units of measures for, two- and three-dimensional objects (i.e., find the perimeter, area, volume).

5. Measurement and Geometry 1.3 Understand the concept of volume and use the appropriate units in common measuring systems (i.e., cubic centimeter [cm^3], cubic meter [m^3], cubic inch [$in.^3$], cubic yard [$yd.^3$]) to compute the volume of rectangular solids.

Math Boxes 10•4

1. Mathematical Reasoning 2.1 Use estimation to verify the reasonableness of calculated results.

2. Mathematical Reasoning 2.0 Students use strategies, skills, and concepts in finding solutions.

3. Number Sense 1.5 Identify and represent on a number line decimals, fractions, mixed numbers, and positive and negative integers.

4. Measurement and Geometry 1.4 Differentiate between, and use appropriate units of measures for, two- and three-dimensional objects (i.e., find the perimeter, area, volume).

5. Measurement and Geometry 1.3 Understand the concept of volume and use the appropriate units in common measuring systems (i.e., cubic centimeter [cm^3], cubic meter [m^3], cubic inch [$in.^3$], cubic yard [$yd.^3$]) to compute the volume of rectangular solids.

Math Boxes 10•5

1. Algebra and Functions 1.2 Use a letter to represent an unknown number; write and evaluate simple algebraic expressions in one variable by substitution.

2. Number Sense 1.3 Understand and compute positive integer powers of nonnegative integers; compute examples as repeated multiplication.

3. Algebra and Functions 1.2 Use a letter to represent an unknown number; write and evaluate simple algebraic expressions in one variable by substitution.

Math Boxes 10✦5 cont.

4. **Mathematical Reasoning 1.1** Analyze problems by identifying relationships, distinguishing relevant from irrelevant information, sequencing and prioritizing information, and observing patterns.

5. **Measurement and Geometry 1.1** Derive and use the formula for the area of a triangle and of a parallelogram by comparing it with the formula for the area of a rectangle (i.e., two of the same triangles make a parallelogram with twice the area; a parallelogram is compared with a rectangle of the same area by cutting and pasting a right triangle on the parallelogram).

Math Boxes 10✦6

1. **Statistics, Data Analysis, and Probability 1.2** Organize and display single-variable data in appropriate graphs and representations (e.g., histogram, circle graphs) and explain which types of graphs are appropriate for various data sets.

2. **Number Sense 2.1** Add, subtract, multiply, and divide with decimals; add with negative integers; subtract positive integers from negative integers; and verify the reasonableness of the results.

3. **Mathematical Reasoning 2.3** Use a variety of methods, such as words, numbers, symbols, charts, graphs, tables, diagrams, and models, to explain mathematical reasoning.

Math Boxes 10✦7

1. **Algebra and Functions 1.2** Use a letter to represent an unknown number; write and evaluate simple algebraic expressions in one variable by substitution.

2. **Number Sense 1.3** Understand and compute positive integer powers of nonnegative integers; compute examples as repeated multiplication.

3. **Algebra and Functions 1.2** Use a letter to represent an unknown number; write and evaluate simple algebraic expressions in one variable by substitution.

4. **Mathematical Reasoning 1.1** Analyze problems by identifying relationships, distinguishing relevant from irrelevant information, sequencing and prioritizing information, and observing patterns.

5. **Measurement and Geometry 1.1** Derive and use the formula for the area of a triangle and of a parallelogram by comparing it with the formula for the area of a rectangle (i.e., two of the same triangles make a parallelogram with twice the area; a parallelogram is compared with a rectangle of the same area by cutting and pasting a right triangle on the parallelogram).

Math Boxes 10✦8

1. **Statistics, Data Analysis, and Probability 1.2** Organize and display single-variable data in appropriate graphs and representations (e.g., histogram, circle graphs) and explain which types of graphs are appropriate for various data sets.

2. **Number Sense 2.1** Add, subtract, multiply, and divide with decimals; add with negative integers; subtract positive integers from negative integers; and verify the reasonableness of the results.

3. **Mathematical Reasoning 2.3** Use a variety of methods, such as words, numbers, symbols, charts, graphs, tables, diagrams, and models, to explain mathematical reasoning.

Math Boxes 10✦9

1. **Algebra and Functions 1.2** Use a letter to represent an unknown number; write and evaluate simple algebraic expressions in one variable by substitution.

2. **Number Sense 1.3** Understand and compute positive integer powers of nonnegative integers; compute examples as repeated multiplication.

3. **Algebra and Functions 1.2** Use a letter to represent an unknown number; write and evaluate simple algebraic expressions in one variable by substitution.

4. **Mathematical Reasoning 1.1** Analyze problems by identifying relationships, distinguishing relevant from irrelevant information, sequencing and prioritizing information, and observing patterns.

5. **Measurement and Geometry 1.3** Understand the concept of volume and use the appropriate units in common measuring systems (i.e., cubic centimeter [cm^3], cubic meter [m^3], cubic inch [$in.^3$], cubic yard [$yd.^3$]) to compute the volume of rectangular solids.

Math Boxes 10✦10

1. **Measurement and Geometry 1.3** Understand the concept of volume and use the appropriate units in common measuring systems (i.e., cubic centimeter [cm^3], cubic meter [m^3], cubic inch [$in.^3$], cubic yard [$yd.^3$]) to compute the volume of rectangular solids.

2. **Measurement and Geometry 2.0** Students identify, describe, and classify the properties of, and the relationships between, plane and solid geometric figures.

3. **Mathematical Reasoning 2.3** Use a variety of methods, such as words, numbers, symbols, charts, graphs, tables, diagrams, and models, to explain mathematical reasoning.

4. **Measurement and Geometry 1.1** Derive and use the formula for the area of a triangle and of a parallelogram by comparing it with the formula for the area of a rectangle (i.e., two of the same triangles make a parallelogram with twice the area; a parallelogram is compared with a rectangle of the same area by cutting and pasting a right triangle on the parallelogram).

Math Boxes 11✦1

1. **Number Sense 2.1** Add, subtract, multiply, and divide with decimals; add with negative integers; subtract positive integers from negative integers; and verify the reasonableness of the results.

2. **Measurement and Geometry 2.1** Measure, identify, and draw angles, perpendicular and parallel lines, rectangles, and triangles by using appropriate tools (e.g., straightedge, ruler, compass, protractor, drawing software).

3. **Statistics, Data Analysis, and Probability 1.2** Organize and display single-variable data in appropriate graphs and representations (e.g., histogram, circle graphs) and explain which types of graphs are appropriate for various data sets.

4. **Number Sense 2.5** Compute and perform simple multiplication and division of fractions and apply these procedures to solving problems.

Math Boxes 11◆1 *cont.*

5. **Number Sense** (1.4) Determine the prime factors of all numbers through 50 and write the numbers as the product of their prime factors by using exponents to show multiples of a factor (e.g., $24 = 2 \times 2 \times 2 \times 3 = 2^3 \times 3$).

Math Boxes 11◆2

1. **Number Sense 2.5** Compute and perform simple multiplication and division of fractions and apply these procedures to solving problems.

2. **Measurement and Geometry** (1.3) Understand the concept of volume and use the appropriate units in common measuring systems (i.e., cubic centimeter [cm^3], cubic meter [m^3], cubic inch [in.^{3}], cubic yard [yd.^{3}]) to compute the volume of rectangular solids.

3. **Mathematical Reasoning 1.1** Analyze problems by identifying relationships, distinguishing relevant from irrelevant information, sequencing and prioritizing information, and observing patterns.

4. **Mathematical Reasoning 2.3** Use a variety of methods, such as words, numbers, symbols, charts, graphs, tables, diagrams, and models, to explain mathematical reasoning.

5. **Number Sense** (1.4) Determine the prime factors of all numbers through 50 and write the numbers as the product of their prime factors by using exponents to show multiples of a factor (e.g., $24 = 2 \times 2 \times 2 \times 3 = 2^3 \times 3$).

6. **Algebra and Functions 1.3** Know and use the distributive property in equations and expressions with variables.

Math Boxes 11◆3

1. **Number Sense** (2.1) Add, subtract, multiply, and divide with decimals; add with negative integers; subtract positive integers from negative integers; and verify the reasonableness of the results.

2. **Measurement and Geometry** (2.1) Measure, identify, and draw angles, perpendicular and parallel lines, rectangles, and triangles by using appropriate tools (e.g., straightedge, ruler, compass, protractor, drawing software).

3. **Statistics, Data Analysis, and Probability 1.2** Organize and display single-variable data in appropriate graphs and representations (e.g., histogram, circle graphs) and explain which types of graphs are appropriate for various data sets.

4. **Number Sense 2.5** Compute and perform simple multiplication and division of fractions and apply these procedures to solving problems.

5. **Number Sense** (1.4) Determine the prime factors of all numbers through 50 and write the numbers as the product of their prime factors by using exponents to show multiples of a factor (e.g., $24 = 2 \times 2 \times 2 \times 3 = 2^3 \times 3$).

Math Boxes 11◆4

1. **Number Sense 2.5** Compute and perform simple multiplication and division of fractions and apply these procedures to solving problems.

2. **Measurement and Geometry** (1.3) Understand the concept of volume and use the appropriate units in common measuring systems (i.e., cubic centimeter [cm^3], cubic meter [m^3], cubic inch [in.^{3}], cubic yard [yd.^{3}]) to compute the volume of rectangular solids.

3. **Mathematical Reasoning 1.1** Analyze problems by identifying relationships, distinguishing relevant from irrelevant information, sequencing and prioritizing information, and observing patterns.

4. **Mathematical Reasoning 2.3** Use a variety of methods, such as words, numbers, symbols, charts, graphs, tables, diagrams, and models, to explain mathematical reasoning.

5. **Number Sense** (1.4) Determine the prime factors of all numbers through 50 and write the numbers as the product of their prime factors by using exponents to show multiples of a factor (e.g., $24 = 2 \times 2 \times 2 \times 3 = 2^3 \times 3$).

6. **Algebra and Functions 1.3** Know and use the distributive property in equations and expressions with variables.

Math Boxes 11◆5

1. **Number Sense** (2.3) Solve simple problems, including ones arising in concrete situations, involving the addition and subtraction of fractions and mixed numbers (like and unlike denominators of 20 or less), and express answers in the simplest form.

2. **Measurement and Geometry** (1.3) Understand the concept of volume and use the appropriate units in common measuring systems (i.e., cubic centimeter [cm^3], cubic meter [m^3], cubic inch [in.^{3}], cubic yard [yd.^{3}]) to compute the volume of rectangular solids.

3. **Measurement and Geometry** (1.3) Understand the concept of volume and use the appropriate units in common measuring systems (i.e., cubic centimeter [cm^3], cubic meter [m^3], cubic inch [in.^{3}], cubic yard [yd.^{3}]) to compute the volume of rectangular solids.

4. **Measurement and Geometry 1.4** Differentiate between, and use appropriate units of measures for, two- and three-dimensional objects (i.e., find the perimeter, area, volume).

5. **Mathematical Reasoning 1.2** Determine when and how to break a problem into simpler parts.

Math Boxes 11◆6

1. **Number Sense 2.5** Compute and perform simple multiplication and division of fractions and apply these procedures to solving problems.

2. **Measurement and Geometry** (1.3) Understand the concept of volume and use the appropriate units in common measuring systems (i.e., cubic centimeter [cm^3], cubic meter [m^3], cubic inch [in.^{3}], cubic yard [yd.^{3}]) to compute the volume of rectangular solids.

3. **Mathematical Reasoning 1.1** Analyze problems by identifying relationships, distinguishing relevant from irrelevant information, sequencing and prioritizing information, and observing patterns.

4. **Mathematical Reasoning 2.3** Use a variety of methods, such as words, numbers, symbols, charts, graphs, tables, diagrams, and models, to explain mathematical reasoning.

5. **Number Sense** (1.4) Determine the prime factors of all numbers through 50 and write the numbers as the product of their prime factors by using exponents to show multiples of a factor (e.g., $24 = 2 \times 2 \times 2 \times 3 = 2^3 \times 3$).

6. **Algebra and Functions 1.3** Know and use the distributive property in equations and expressions with variables.

Math Boxes 11•7

1. **Number Sense 2.3** Solve simple problems, including ones arising in concrete situations, involving the addition and subtraction of fractions and mixed numbers (like and unlike denominators of 20 or less), and express answers in the simplest form.
2. **Mathematical Reasoning 2.4** Express the solution clearly and logically by using the appropriate mathematical notation and terms and clear language; support solutions with evidence in both verbal and symbolic work.
3. **Measurement and Geometry 1.3** Understand the concept of volume and use the appropriate units in common measuring systems (i.e., cubic centimeter [cm^3], cubic meter [m^3], cubic inch [$in.^3$], cubic yard [$yd.^3$]) to compute the volume of rectangular solids.
4. **Measurement and Geometry 1.4** Differentiate between, and use appropriate units of measures for, two- and three-dimensional objects (i.e., find the perimeter, area, volume).
5. **Mathematical Reasoning 1.2** Determine when and how to break a problem into simpler parts.

Math Boxes 11•8

1. **Number Sense 1.2** Interpret percents as part of a hundred; find decimal and percent equivalents for common fractions and explain why they represent the same value; compute a given percent of a whole number.
2. **Number Sense 1.4** Determine the prime factors of all numbers through 50 and write the numbers as the product of their prime factors by using exponents to show multiples of a factor (e.g., $24 = 2 \times 2 \times 2 \times 3 = 2^3 \times 3$).
3. **Number Sense 1.3** Understand and compute positive integer powers of nonnegative integers; compute examples as repeated multiplication.
4. **Number Sense 1.4** Determine the prime factors of all numbers through 50 and write the numbers as the product of their prime factors by using exponents to show multiples of a factor (e.g., $24 = 2 \times 2 \times 2 \times 3 = 2^3 \times 3$).
5. **Number Sense 2.5** Compute and perform simple multiplication and division of fractions and apply these procedures to solving problems.
6. **Mathematical Reasoning 1.0** Students make decisions about how to approach problems.

Math Boxes 12•1

1. **Number Sense 1.2** Interpret percents as part of a hundred; find decimal and percent equivalents for common fractions and explain why they represent the same value; compute a given percent of a whole number.
2. **Mathematical Reasoning 2.2** Apply strategies and results from simpler problems to more complex problems.
3. **Number Sense 1.5** Identify and represent on a number line decimals, fractions, mixed numbers, and positive and negative integers.
4. **Mathematical Reasoning 2.3** Use a variety of methods, such as words, numbers, symbols, charts, graphs, tables, diagrams, and models, to explain mathematical reasoning.

Math Boxes 12•2

1. **Mathematical Reasoning 2.1** Use estimation to verify the reasonableness of calculated results.
2. **Measurement and Geometry 2.1** Measure, identify, and draw angles, perpendicular and parallel lines, rectangles, and triangles by using appropriate tools (e.g., straightedge, ruler, compass, protractor, drawing software).
3. **Mathematical Reasoning 2.2** Apply strategies and results from simpler problems to more complex problems.
4. **Measurement and Geometry 1.0** Students understand and compute the volumes and areas of simple objects.

Math Boxes 12•3

1. **Number Sense 1.2** Interpret percents as part of a hundred; find decimal and percent equivalents for common fractions and explain why they represent the same value; compute a given percent of a whole number.
2. **Mathematical Reasoning 2.2** Apply strategies and results from simpler problems to more complex problems.
3. **Number Sense 1.5** Identify and represent on a number line decimals, fractions, mixed numbers, and positive and negative integers.
4. **Mathematical Reasoning 2.3** Use a variety of methods, such as words, numbers, symbols, charts, graphs, tables, diagrams, and models, to explain mathematical reasoning.

Math Boxes 12•4

1. **Mathematical Reasoning 2.1** Use estimation to verify the reasonableness of calculated results.
2. **Measurement and Geometry 2.1** Measure, identify, and draw angles, perpendicular and parallel lines, rectangles, and triangles by using appropriate tools (e.g., straightedge, ruler, compass, protractor, drawing software).
3. **Mathematical Reasoning 2.2** Apply strategies and results from simpler problems to more complex problems.
4. **Measurement and Geometry 1.0** Students understand and compute the volumes and areas of simple objects.

Math Boxes 12•5

1. **Number Sense 2.5** Compute and perform simple multiplication and division of fractions and apply these procedures to solving problems.
2. **Mathematical Reasoning 1.1** Analyze problems by identifying relationships, distinguishing relevant from irrelevant information, sequencing and prioritizing information, and observing patterns.
3. **Mathematical Reasoning 2.5** Indicate the relative advantages of exact and approximate solutions to problems and give answers to a specified degree of accuracy.
4. **Mathematical Reasoning 2.2** Apply strategies and results from simpler problems to more complex problems.
5. **Algebra and Functions 1.5** Solve problems involving linear functions with integer values; write the equation; and graph the resulting ordered pairs of integers on a grid.

Math Boxes 12•6

1. Algebra and Functions (1.4) Identify and graph ordered pairs in the four quadrants of the coordinate plane.

2. Number Sense 2.5 Compute and perform simple multiplication and division of fractions and apply these procedures to solving problems.

3. Measurement and Geometry (2.2) Know that the sum of the angles of any triangle is 180° and the sum of the angles of any quadrilateral is 360° and use this information to solve problems.

4. Number Sense (1.2) Interpret percents as part of a hundred; find decimal and percent equivalents for common fractions and explain why they represent the same value; compute a given percent of a whole number.

5. Number Sense (1.5) Identify and represent on a number line decimals, fractions, mixed numbers, and positive and negative integers.

Math Boxes 12•7

1. Number Sense 2.5 Compute and perform simple multiplication and division of fractions and apply these procedures to solving problems.

2. Mathematical Reasoning 1.1 Analyze problems by identifying relationships, distinguishing relevant from irrelevant information, sequencing and prioritizing information, and observing patterns.

3. Mathematical Reasoning 2.5 Indicate the relative advantages of exact and approximate solutions to problems and give answers to a specified degree of accuracy.

4. Mathematical Reasoning 2.2 Apply strategies and results from simpler problems to more complex problems.

5. Algebra and Functions (1.5) Solve problems involving linear functions with integer values; write the equation; and graph the resulting ordered pairs of integers on a grid.

Math Boxes 12•8

1. Algebra and Functions (1.4) Identify and graph ordered pairs in the four quadrants of the coordinate plane.

2. Number Sense 2.5 Compute and perform simple multiplication and division of fractions and apply these procedures to solving problems.

3. Measurement and Geometry (2.2) Know that the sum of the angles of any triangle is 180° and the sum of the angles of any quadrilateral is 360° and use this information to solve problems.

4. Number Sense (1.2) Interpret percents as part of a hundred; find decimal and percent equivalents for common fractions and explain why they represent the same value; compute a given percent of a whole number.

5. Number Sense (1.5) Identify and represent on a number line decimals, fractions, mixed numbers, and positive and negative integers.

Math Boxes 12•9

1. Mathematical Reasoning 2.3 Use a variety of methods, such as words, numbers, symbols, charts, graphs, tables, diagrams, and models, to explain mathematical reasoning.

2. Measurement and Geometry 1.4 Differentiate between, and use appropriate units of measures for, two- and three-dimensional objects (i.e., find the perimeter, area, volume).

3. Number Sense (2.3) Solve simple problems, including ones arising in concrete situations, involving the addition and subtraction of fractions and mixed numbers (like and unlike denominators of 20 or less), and express answers in the simplest form.

4. Number Sense 2.4 Understand the concept of multiplication and division of fractions.

5. Mathematical Reasoning 2.4 Express the solution clearly and logically by using the appropriate mathematical notation and terms and clear language; support solutions with evidence in both verbal and symbolic work.

6. Number Sense (2.1) Add, subtract, multiply, and divide with decimals; add with negative integers; subtract positive integers from negative integers; and verify the reasonableness of the results.

Slide Rule

Assembly Instructions

1. Cut along the solid lines.

2. Score and fold along the dashed line of the holder so the number lines are on the outside.

Slider

Holder

Integer Holder

Fraction Holder

Fraction Slider

Integer Slider

Rectangular Prism Patterns

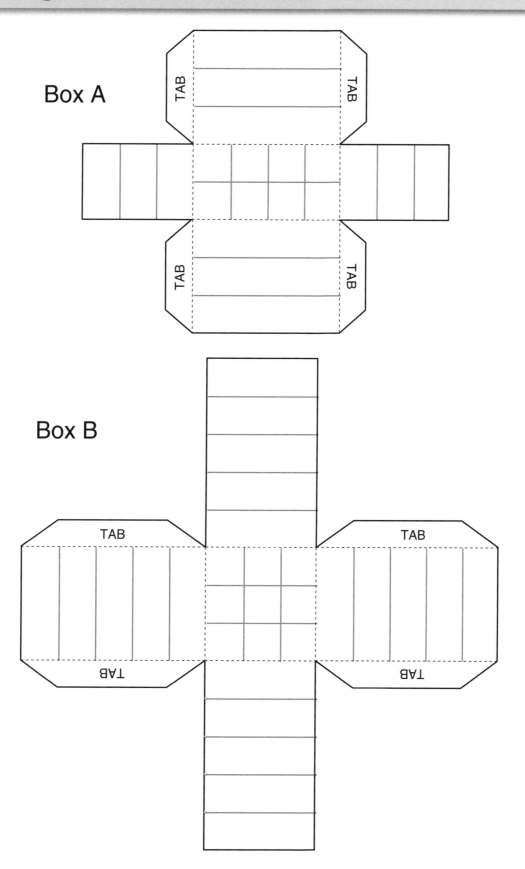

Box A

Box B

Square Tiles

Spoon Scramble Cards

$\frac{1}{4}$ of 24	$\frac{3}{4} * 8$	50% of 12	$0.10 * 60$
$\frac{1}{3}$ of 21	$3\frac{1}{2} * 2$	25% of 28	$0.10 * 70$
$\frac{1}{5}$ of 40	$2 * \frac{16}{4}$	1% of 800	$0.10 * 80$
$\frac{3}{4}$ of 12	$4\frac{1}{2} * 2$	25% of 36	$0.10 * 90$

Activity Sheet 8